# The New Physician

THE GRAND ROUNDS PRESS®

# The New Physician

## Teo Furtado

WHITTLE DIRECT BOOKS

Photographs: Dr. Alan J. Pomerance, page 15: Cameron Wood; Dr. Ron R. Loeppke, page 25: Fritz
Hoffmann; Dr. Francine R. Gaillour, page 34: Rex Rystedt; Dr. Ross L. Egger, page 46: Ilene Ehrlich;
Dr. Andrew J. K. Smith, page 57: Keri Pickett; Dr. Brian E. Ely, page 67: Jamie Tanaka.

The Grand Rounds Press: Dorothy Foltz-Gray, Editor;
Ken Smith, Design Director; Susan Brill, Art Director

The Grand Rounds Press is a registered trademark of Whittle Communications L.P.

Library of Congress Catalog Card Number: 94-60573
Furtado, Teo
The New Physician
ISBN 1-879736-24-1
ISSN 1053-6620

# The Grand Rounds Press

The Grand Rounds Press publishes original short books by distinguished authors on subjects of importance to the medical profession. This year Grand Rounds presents MD/2000, a special series of four books designed to help doctors make sense of the rapid changes occurring in the U.S. health care delivery system.

Grand Rounds Press books, which appear approximately every three months, are edited and published by Whittle Books, a business unit of Whittle Communications L.P. They reflect a broad spectrum of responsible opinions. In each book the opinions expressed are those of the author, not the publisher or advertiser.

I welcome your comments on this unique endeavor.

*William S. Rukeyser*
*Editor in Chief*

*For my wife, Barbara, to whom I owe everything.*

*And with special thanks to Dorothy Foltz-Gray, one of the most wonderful editors—and friends—any writer could hope for. She remained supportive throughout and kept her humor when mine was in short supply.*

# contents

# *introduction*

As managed care has taken root in the U.S., the working lives of doctors have changed dramatically. Many have moved from a private practice they thought would last a lifetime to some form of integrated practice. To make such a move, doctors have had to reexamine who they are as physicians and as people. What are the skills they will need in the new world of managed care? How will they make the transition from private practitioner to team player? Will they become better doctors or cost-conscious bureaucrats? Will they lose touch with patient care as they learn to simultaneously consider cost?

Most doctors anticipate the transition with trepidation. Yet perhaps their fears are exaggerated. As the conversations with physicians that form the heart of this book demonstrate, doctors can take advantage of the widespread changes in the medical system and further their ambition as healers without diminishing their income, sense of competence, independence, or quality of care.

All six of the physicians interviewed are continuing to redefine their role as caregivers. One cofounded an independent-practice association. Others became more involved in management and policymaking and thereby changed the course of their organizations. One found she could be a powerful advocate for patient care and physician control, even within a large health-maintenance organization. What they share is an unwillingness to wait for change. And each is convinced that the doctor who is prepared need not fear the new health care environment.

The journey from private practice to managed care can take many forms. In the mid-1980s obstetrician Alan J. Pomerance of Atlanta faced an intensely competitive urban market. As he pieced together a new professional identity, joining PPOs and HMOs and forming an independent-practice association, he also grappled with the scorn of peers who viewed his transition as a form of treason.

Dr. Ron R. Loeppke, a specialist in preventive and occupational medicine, began his practice at a five-doctor clinic in Seattle. As managed care evolved, so did Loeppke's thinking. Now corporate medical director and vice-president of health affairs at PhyCor, he has acted on his conviction that by focusing on the health of populations rather than individual patients he can make a greater contribution to medicine.

Like many doctors, internist Francine R. Gaillour feared becoming a faceless number when she left a private practice she loved to work part time for the Group Health Cooperative of Puget Sound. Her experience illustrates how doctors can retain a sense of power and influence within a managed-care system.

Dr. Ross L. Egger also left private practice, after 24 years as a small-town family practitioner, to become the medical director of Blue Cross and Blue Shield of Indiana. Although he has since returned to private practice, his five years with Blue Cross retooled his thinking about health care reform. His transitions represent one way of dealing with the frustration and anger that many doctors feel when confronted by insurance rules and regulations.

The fifth doctor, neurosurgeon Andrew J. K. Smith of Minneapolis, despaired of finding a place within a managed-care system that would allow him to retain his independence. In 1993 he lost half his practice when a hospital he worked for merged with a large multispecialty clinic. Like many doctors, he realized that shaping a new identity was crucial to his survival. His formation of a

750-doctor clinic without walls—a group practice operating from multiple sites—has allowed him to envision a new role for himself and many other independent doctors who want to avoid selling their practices or signing exclusive contracts.

The story of Dr. Brian E. Ely, a family practitioner in Sacramento, California, confirms that the transition to managed care can be made by degrees. When Ely began his practice in the mid-1980s, he focused, like most physicians, on his relationship with individual patients, not large questions about the future of health care. As he realized how much medicine was changing, he decided to become an agent of change rather than its victim. He joined the Sacramento-Sierra Medical Group in 1986, hoping for a way to remain independent and to maintain control over his practice. Now, as medical director of the Sutter Medical Foundation, he has transferred his focus to directing change.

For these physicians, as for most of their colleagues, change hasn't been easy or smooth. Several have had to struggle to retain the autonomy they once enjoyed as independent practitioners. Some have suffered anxiety and grief. They have had to learn new skills and assume new roles, to think of themselves as team players rather than lone rangers. But each has come to realize that in the new environment, doctors can have real clout—if they are willing to rethink who they are and who they can become.

# CHAPTER one

# SURVIVING A TIGHT MARKET

D
r. Alan Pomerance had just opened his practice when the first waves of HMOs and PPOs began to transform the medical landscape of Atlanta. As he started losing one or two patients a month, he could see what the future held. With trepidation he agreed to join some of the plans—a difficult decision because, like many other physicians in the region, he worried that his colleagues would treat him as a pariah. Atlanta in 1983 was a medically conservative community, and those who dared affiliate with PPOs—or anything else that smacked of managed care—were, as he said, branded "outcasts and traitors to the profession."

A feisty, practical man, Pomerance risked the opprobrium of his colleagues and has managed to ride the health care roller coaster successfully, making a transition that he never expected as a medical student. (His early interest was pediatrics, but that changed the day he operated on a German shepherd as part of a research project. "Having living tissue in my hands, helping to repair it, knowing that the animal was going to get better as a result—I was hooked on surgery," he said.)

As the following conversation makes clear, the 44-year-old obstetrician has learned how to negotiate managed-care contracts, survive the intrusions of utilization review, and adapt his practice to keep his patients. In addition he and several colleagues are form-

*Dr. Alan J. Pomerance*
*Obstetrician*

ing an independent-practice association as an alternative to the increasingly closed panels of HMOs and PPOs. Pomerance is convinced that doctors can take charge of their practices and control the debate on managed care if they are willing to act. "Doctors don't have to put up with bullying tactics," he said.

*When and why did you first become involved with managed care?*
DR. POMERANCE: Around 1983, not long after I'd begun my own practice in obstetric gynecology, HMOs started popping up in Atlanta. I soon noticed a disturbing trend: I was losing an average of

one or two patients each month to an HMO. The patients said they were sorry to leave, but they had to because their employers had switched coverage. I couldn't afford any drain on my practice, no matter how small, so I contacted AmeriPlan and Georgia Medical Plan [now Cigna Healthplan of Georgia], two open-panel HMOs, about joining. Now between 40 and 50 percent of our patients belong to a PPO. About 10 percent come from an HMO, and 5 percent are on Medicaid or Medicare. The remainder belong to traditional insurers.

*How have you felt about the transition?*

At first, there was little to complain about. The HMOs did what even their critics would call a reasonably good job. The system had a lot of fat in the early 1980s, a lot of unnecessary expenses. It wasn't uncommon, for example, for a woman in her forties to be hospitalized for irregular bleeding, have a D and C the following day, and be discharged the day after. That meant she stayed three days in the hospital for a minor procedure. People whose problems were not life-threatening were admitted for two or three days for X-rays and consultations instead of receiving treatment as outpatients. The HMOs trimmed a lot of that fat, and they were able to save—and make—a lot of money in the process.

*And that was a threat to private practitioners?*

On the contrary. For doctors like me who had contracted with the HMOs it worked out very well: we'd get a nice little check at the end of the year because we were doing a good job, and the HMOs had made money. That was in addition to the income from our regular fee-for-service patients.

*So HMOs came in, boosted efficiency, reduced waste, and increased doctors' incomes. What happened?*

That began to change, in part because the rest of the medical community realized it had to become more efficient to compete with the HMOs. And although HMOs did manage to reduce costs during the 1980s, technological improvements and increased salaries for nurses and ancillary staff members reduced some of that savings. As a result, it became harder and harder for the HMOs to

*He published four volumes,
but he's best known for two words.*

Miles is proud to present this series on...

# Powerful
# Innovators

# Powerful Physician

*Hans Christian Joachim Gram (1853-1938)*

The words "Gram's stain" are familiar to all physicians, but few know of the man behind the method.

A native of Copenhagen, Gram earned his medical degree at its University, then traveled in Europe, studying pharmacology and bacteriology.

In 1884, while working in Berlin, he published a paper describing his now-famous microbiologic staining method. While his technique was derived from Paul Ehrlich's staining of the tubercle bacillus, Gram's method proved applicable to <u>all</u> bacteria.

Gram returned to Copenhagen, where he became a popular professor and physician, and published a four-volume work on rational pharmacotherapy in clinical science. But his most significant work had already been done: the Gram method remains a first step in classifying and identifying bacteria, as well as assisting in determining the treatment of bacterial diseases.

# Powerful Antimicrobial

Speed...power...efficacy against urinary tract infections,* whatever the severity, and efficacy against mild to moderate lower respiratory and skin and skin structure infections.* That's the power of Cipro® I.V.  The power that can make the difference in your practice.

# Powerful Numbers

*speak for themselves:*

**100**...*Percent of patients whose severe urinary tract infections\* resolved or improved[†] after 5.6 days of Cipro® I.V. therapy[‡] in a recent Multicenter Study.[4]*

**95**...*Percent of patients whose mild to moderate respiratory tract infections\* resolved or improved[†] after 6.6 days of Cipro® I.V. therapy[‡] in a recent Multicenter Study.[4]*

**95**...*Percent of patients whose mild to moderate skin and skin structure infections\* resolved or improved[†] after 7.2 days of Cipro® I.V. therapy[‡] in a recent Multicenter Study.[4]*

The most potent fluoroquinolone.[1-3][§]

*Please see complete prescribing information and cited references at the end of this book.*

In clinical studies, the most frequently reported events, without regard to drug relationship, among patients treated with intravenous ciprofloxacin were nausea, diarrhea, central nervous system disturbance, local iv site reactions, abnormalities of liver associated enzymes (hepatic enzymes), and eosinophilia. Headache, restlessness, and rash were also noted in greater than 1% of patients treated with the most common doses of ciprofloxacin.

\*Due to susceptible strains of indicated pathogens. See indicated organisms and dosage and administration sections in complete prescribing information.

[†]Clinical response at the end of I.V. therapy (400 mg q12h). "Resolution" defined as disappearance or sufficient reduction of all signs and symptoms of infection to allow discontinuance of antimicrobial therapy; "improvement" defined as reduction in severity/number of signs and symptoms, but requiring continued antimicrobial therapy. Most "improved" patients were then switched to Cipro® oral therapy. Resolutions at posttreatment evaluations were 85.3% for lower respiratory infections, 92.9% for urinary tract infections, and 92.9% for skin and skin structure infections.

[‡]Average duration of Cipro® I.V. therapy.

[§]*In vitro* activity does not necessarily imply a correlation with *in vivo* results.

Miles Inc.
Pharmaceutical Division
400 Morgan Lane
West Haven, CT 06516

make as much profit, so they started demanding more discounts for care and became more intrusive.

Suddenly we couldn't do surgery or admit patients to a hospital without precertification and in-hospital reviews; consultations with physicians not on the plans were restricted. And the HMOs added primary doctors who served as gatekeepers, further cutting specialists' access to patients. Many doctors felt squeezed out.

*What impact did preferred-provider organizations have?*

Generally we liked dealing with the PPOs because at the time they intruded so little into our practices. If I was on the list of preferred providers for a patient, for example, and picked up on a cardiac problem during an examination, I could refer the patient to Dr. X if I thought he was the best cardiologist for that problem—even if he wasn't on the plan. With an HMO, referring out of plan was a bureaucratic nightmare.

*How were doctors recruited by these plans?*

In the beginning, when closed-panel HMOs were getting organized, they advertised on local TV and radio. They would talk about how they'd hand-chosen doctors for their dedication and professionalism. But their pitch to doctors was something altogether different. For about six months, I'd get mailings saying, "These are the benefits for you as a doctor: guaranteed time off, guaranteed nights off. Your day ends at five o'clock when you're not on call."

So they were recruiting doctors by promising good vacations and lots of time off, yet they were advertising to patients about the dedicated, personalized staff. I said, "Gee, I wish the newspapers would run that pitch to doctors right opposite the ad for patients."

*How did PPOs recruit?*

Fliers were everywhere about joining this or that PPO. Sometimes a doctor already on a panel would give them my name. Other times a patient would enroll in a PPO and recommend me for its list. Toward the end of the 1980s, a lot of us would receive unsolicited letters and contracts from the PPOs and insurance companies saying, "We are establishing a PPO network in your area. These are the benefits of joining. Here's a contract."

The offer to many doctors was nearly irresistible. For one thing, they'd tell you that the company would never mail its checks to the patient. All payments would go to you.

*How did you negotiate the contracts with these new companies?*

Initially there wasn't much negotiation. Some of the plan representatives wouldn't even tell you what the fees were. You'd get the contract accompanied by a list of procedure codes, you'd put down what your fees were for those procedures, and the companies told you whether you were in their range. Most doctors in the early 1980s were novices about subcontracting and didn't think to negotiate about the fees even a little bit.

That has changed to some extent. My partners and I, for example, have started crossing out or altering points in a contract we disagree with. If we don't like a paragraph, we'll cross out a word or two and fill in a word we like. We've found that our revisions will be accepted much of the time. One company, for example, included a clause in the contract giving them the right to audit our financial records. We crossed that out and wrote "financial records only pertaining to patients insured by the company." They also wanted the right to examine our charts for utilization and review. We added "only with advance notice and only in regard to patients covered by the company." With those kinds of issues, you have more leeway than with fees.

*You mentioned that you and others at first embraced PPOs. Has the romance faded?*

It lasted for a while. We liked the independence they offered and the relative freedom from hassles. But the number of PPOs and HMOs in Atlanta grew too large, too quickly. Toward the end of the 1980s and the early 1990s, HMOs and PPOs had almost 45 percent of the market share. So they started closing their doors to nonaligned physicians and began trimming those who were affiliated.

That's had a direct impact on my practice, especially because the PPOs and HMOs also began limiting the hospitals on the plan. My practice—Perimeter Ob-Gyn Associates—is across the street from a small, 150-bed hospital run by the Hospital Corporation of America and three and a half miles away from a 500-bed community hospital. When the HCA hospital was built in 1990, my two partners and I moved most of our practice there because it was convenient, especially when we had a patient in labor. It was wonderful going on rounds and then walking across the street to our offices.

But some of the private hospitals—for whatever reason—were not able to get or keep many PPO contracts. And when a hospital loses a contract to another hospital, the patients usually follow the contract. That forces my partners and me to make a choice. Do we want to lose the patient or drive four miles through city streets? If we are providers on a PPO's list, we get the same money no matter where we deliver.

*But it was your choice, right?*

Not really. When some plans decided to contract with the community hospital, they did not renew our contracts. They wrote us a letter saying, "We are severing our relationship with the HCA hospital and with you." Essentially they said, "We're moving the whole shebang down the road," not "Gee, you guys are the most expensive guys in town and we can't have you on the plan anymore." We were losing our contract just because of our affiliation with a particular hospital. We'd call back and say, "We'll be glad to deliver care at the other hospital." They'd say, "Well, we have enough doctors there anyway. Don't worry about it. Forget it. Goodbye."

I've been lucky though. My partners and I have managed to stay on the panel of enough PPOs so that the practice hasn't been harmed. But it's a significant inconvenience because now we have to have a backup call system in case patients are in labor at both hospitals.

*You've talked about how intrusive some of these plans became. How do they compare with traditional insurance companies?*

It's true that managed-care organizations can be intrusive, but indemnity insurers also have physician review. They approve some procedures automatically. For others—such as hysterectomies, hospital D and C's, and gallbladder operations—they may want special reviews, and you have to inform them of what you're planning.

Here's an example that shows how absurd the review process can get. I once did a woman's tubal ligation. I saw that she had endometriosis, but she had no symptoms. Over the next six years, she did begin to show intermittent symptoms, and I felt she needed a hysterectomy. She was over 40 and didn't want children, so she had no problem with having the operation. I called up the physician review people, who said, "No, that doesn't meet our criteria."

"Well, I'd like a doctor review," I said. A doctor called me and told me that we hadn't proved the endometriosis was causing her problem; what she needed was a laparoscopy.

"I did a laparoscopy six years ago when I tied her tubes and found endometriosis," I told him.

"That was six years ago; this is now."

"That's just a waste of this woman's time and money," I said.

"You have to do this," he answered.

I asked for an appeal. They concluded she needed a second opinion and gave her a choice of physicians. She called one office where the physician on the list couldn't see her, but his partner could. "Yes, everything points to endometriosis," he told her. "You need to have the hysterectomy." But this physician was fresh out of residency and not yet board-certified, so the insurance company wouldn't accept his opinion. They agreed to pay the woman for her visit but insisted that she go back to see the other doctor. He told her the same thing: "Absolutely, you need to have a hysterectomy. Go have it done." Only then did the insurer approve the operation.

But the same thing happens with HMOs and PPOs. One HMO I'm affiliated with authorized three days' stay for one of my patients to have a hysterectomy. The patient was doing reasonably well, but on the morning of the third day her abdomen was distended; she hadn't been passing gas well and had just started eating solid food that morning. On the third day, I got a phone call from the HMO's physician reviewer asking why she was still in the hospital. I explained her situation.

"Has she had one solid meal and kept it down?" he asked.

"Yes, one so far."

"According to our criteria, that's reason enough to be discharged."

"The American College of Obstetricians and Gynecologists has a position statement saying that 24 hours on a prescribed diet without nausea and vomiting is required before discharge," I answered. "I've got a patient here who until today couldn't tolerate solid food."

That wasn't good enough. "As you know, Doctor, you can get hospital-acquired bacteria in hospitals, and our goal is to protect the patient, to get her out of the hospital, because hospitals are dangerous places," he said.

This woman wasn't ready to go home, and I kept her an extra day; the insurance company refused to pay. Of course when she got the bill from the hospital a couple of months later, after the insurance finally paid its part minus a day's charges, she came in yelling at me about it. Fortunately, I had documented her situation on the hospital chart: "Patient feels very bad. Does not feel like she can go home." I showed it to her.

"This is what you told me that morning when I made rounds in the hospital," I explained. "You were not feeling well enough to go home. I can't predict the future; I can't predict what the insurance company is going to pay." She finally paid the bill and has come back for yearly visits since.

Every doctor can probably tell you a similar story, but to tell the truth, this was the only time I've had a problem I haven't been able to work out with an HMO or a PPO.

*With everything you've experienced, would you advise a doctor to affiliate with a managed-care plan?*

I don't think there's any question: the best thing a private practitioner in an area like Atlanta can do is join as many PPOs as he can handle. If you can live with a PPO's prices and utilization-review criteria, join. If you don't join when you're invited, in a year or two it may be too late. If you wait until your patients start leaving you to join a PPO, you may be told, "Sorry, we have enough doctors in this area."

*Tell me about the independent-practice association you and several doctors are developing. When and why did you start it?*

In 1993, when a couple of obstetricians had the idea of forming an IPA, my partners and I liked the idea. We started by looking at a map of the city, located doctors in each area who were not competing against each other—doctors on the northeast side of town versus the southwest side of town—and sent out feelers to see how much interest there was in forming a corporate structure. We felt that we could interest payers—large insurance companies or major employers—in contracting with us to provide obstetrical and gynecological care to their employees.

The response among physicians has been extraordinary. But private payers, the big industries, are babes in the wood. The concept is brand-new for them. That does worry me because I can imagine our marketing representative going to a benefits executive at Coca-Cola, for example, and having the executive say, "I don't know about this." He's not likely to change and be experimental. This IPA is on the cutting edge, but how viable it is, I don't know.

*How far along is the development?*

We've hired a consulting firm, which is trying to market the concept, and contacted an insurance company—we're still negotiating with them. They liked the idea but wanted wider geographical coverage. We went back out to recruit more doctors and submitted a proposal to the company. My partners and I spend considerable time now interviewing organizations that want to join and talking to lawyers about the setup.

*How would it be integrated?*

This IPA is unusual: it's laterally integrated. In other words, we've concentrated on recruiting other obstetricians and gynecologists. It's a risk because payers may be more interested in a vertically integrated system with a base of primary-care physicians. We don't know how it's going to work out.

*What risk is involved in this venture?*

Each of us has invested $1,500 for start-up costs. If we never get a contract, that's all we're at risk for. Later the risk will be greater. Let's say some company says, "Okay, you guys can handle all our ob-gyn work for the year. We've got 50,000 women in the reproductive age group and will tell them they have to go to

*Dr. Ron R. Loeppke*
*Preventive and Occupational Medicine*

patients to managing the health of whole populations, in essence he has become one of the ultimate team players in the new world of managed medicine.

*What was your view of medicine when you graduated from the University of Kansas School of Medicine in 1979?*

DR LOEPPKE: I had a great deal of idealism about what it meant to be a doctor. It was a privilege and honor. But I felt an almost overwhelming sense of responsibility to those entrusting their lives to me. My purpose was to save lives and stamp out disease—at any cost. In fact, when it came to human life and suffering, I thought cost should not even be an issue. I should do everything possible to help a patient, and doing more was always better than not doing enough.

*When and how did your ideas begin to change?*

I recognized the need to emphasize prevention during my clinical training. All too often I would treat patients in the emergency room whose conditions could have been prevented. I realized that what I did for them was overshadowed by their lifestyle and health behaviors, their mundane habits of daily life. It became increasingly frustrating to interact with people in moments of crisis. I concluded that my idealistic view had to change. I had to go beyond what I could do *to* people and shift to what I could do *with* people so that they could help themselves.

By the time I joined Greeley Medical Clinic after a few years of practice, I realized I could be more effective as part of a multispecialty clinical team, part of a system of care. We could offer economies and qualities of scale through shared best practices instead of depending on isolated events of care.

When I attended the University of Washington program in public health, it emphasized issues of health planning, behavior, and economics. Many of my courses were taught by professors who also taught courses for the executive MBA program. Their business approach to health care was very illuminating.

Doctors are sailing into uncharted waters. We cannot alter the winds of change, but we can adjust the sails. Change is going to occur whether doctors want it or not. So the important thing is to learn how to navigate and make the transformation good for all parties.

I guess I'm a pioneer. I've learned to enjoy the challenge of change and its opportunity. It has been an empowering transition and I feel free to face the inevitable next passage.

*How were you involved in Greeley Medical Clinic's transition to managed care?*

In 1990, the year we joined PhyCor, managed care was still anathema to many doctors, but most of us at GMC recognized that our involvement would increase and we'd better learn how to deal with it. We also realized that if we wanted to move crisply in the marketplace, we needed to have the management and business expertise to analyze data, trends, and issues, and we needed money to effect management decisions. Our clinic didn't have enough of either at the time.

We considered going to a bank, raising venture capital, or affiliating with a hospital. But PhyCor works with multispecialty clinics and group practices so we contacted them, and they agreed to join us as a fully vested partner.

In January 1994 I became PhyCor's medical director, a position I took with mixed emotions because I'm no longer providing direct patient care. It has been hard to give up my clinic practice, but I also feel energized by the possibility of helping physicians affect health care trends and policies and improving health care for populations of people, not just individual patients.

*Describe the program you started at GMC.*

I started CHAMPS in 1988. My idea was to provide comprehensive clinical, occupational, and preventive medical services to regional and national corporations. When I started there in 1987, GMC was working with about 50 companies. By the end of 1993, the program had expanded to more than 1,000 companies.

Corporate health will be the cornerstone of any restructured health care system. Doctors are going to be more engaged with all members of the health system: primary-care and specialty providers, hospitals and insurance companies, employers and employees and their families. We have to assume shared accountability.

Physicians will become more accountable through outcomes measurement and continuous quality improvement, making sure that we offer cost-effective, high-quality care. Doctors have an increasing opportunity to become involved with employers who purchase health care by helping companies understand the financial and health impact of clinical decisions. In fact, employers will seek out physicians to fill the role of "corporate health officer," a liaison and translator who can take issues from the examination room and communicate them to the boardroom.

*Isn't that what CHAMPS is all about?*

Yes. But I don't want you to think that when I talk about shared accountability I'm restricting myself to doctors. Companies and employees have an equal role to play. Employers have to try, for example, to prevent some of the repetitive-motion, cumulative-trauma disorders rampant in the workplace. They have to address environmental issues, such as toxic exposure.

Many times it's sick workplaces that lead to sick workers. And I'm not just talking about exposure to chemicals, but about things like stress and dysfunctional relationships between supervisors and employees. You see the results of such problems in clinics, where many people express work dissatisfaction through lower back pain.

Employees and their families also need to participate. We have to help them improve their lifestyles to reduce their health risks or to minimize the effects of a problem they have little control over.

*By preventive medicine and shared accountability, you're not talking about just doing more yearly physical exams?*

By no means. Health care organizations need to participate in health-risk appraisals of the populations they serve, identify those who are at risk, and then do health screenings based on age, sex, and risk.

A lot of discussion about reform has focused on cost. But little is said about the participants in the health care system. If we can form a true partnership among the patient, the provider, and the purchaser of care, we can reduce cost and waste and improve health. We've got to think of ourselves as excellent providers not only of medical care, but also of health care.

*That's a big order, especially because not all doctors have training in preventive medicine.*

That's true, but I think the health care system of the 21st century will be built on the pillars of preventive medicine, so we must prepare. In fact, the restructuring that will occur in health care will demand that we keep people as healthy as possible—not just be-

*"I have worked as hard as I could...
if my success has been greater than
that of most...the reason is that I came
in my wanderings through the medical field upon regions where the gold
was still lying by the wayside...and
that is of no great merit."*

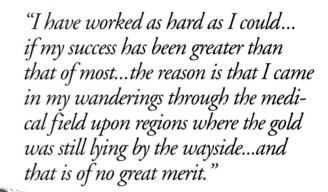

Miles is proud to present this series on...

# Powerful Innovators

# Powerful Physician

*Robert Koch (1843-1910)*

*Even Koch himself would have been surprised to learn in 1866 that he would become one of the most important bacteriologists of all time. His dream of traveling to exotic ports took an ironic turn when his wife's gift of a microscope spurred his interest in the exotic world of microbes.*

*With a passionate interest in bacteriology generated by a crisis that struck in 1876 (an anthrax epidemic among local cattle), Koch studied the disease, cultured the organism on artificial media, analyzed its complete life cycle, and transferred the infection to mice.*

*Koch's research in bacteriology continued: He isolated and cultivated staphylococci from surgical infections, analyzed streptococci taken from wound exudate, and discovered the bacillus that causes conjunctivitis. Perhaps his most important contribution was the discovery of the bacillus responsible for tuberculosis, a devastating illness at that time.*

# Powerful Antimicrobial

*Cipro® gives you the power you need to eradicate causative pathogens of skin infections.\*  With its excellent penetration of blister fluid,† Cipro® is <u>proven</u> effective monotherapy for many patients with skin/skin structure infections beyond the reach of traditional first-line antibiotics.‡*

# Cipro® TABLETS
## (ciprofloxacin HCl)

**The most potent fluoroquinolone.**[1-3§]

# Powerful Numbers

*Speak for themselves*

**12** *...Number of hours serum concentrations of Cipro® are maintained in excess of MIC$_{90s}$ of susceptible bacteria.*

**40** *...Cipro® peak skin blister fluid concentration is at least 40% higher than the MIC$_{90s}$ of most common bacteria.[†]*

**96** *...The percentage of favorable clinical response (resolution + improvement) with Cipro® reported in skin infections such as infected ulcer, postoperative wounds, cellulitis, infected burns, and abscesses.*

**250/500/750** *...Dosage strengths of Cipro® Tablets available.*

**Cipro®** TABLETS
(ciprofloxacin HCl)

**The most potent fluoroquinolone.[1-3§]**

*See complete prescribing information at the end of this book.*

**THE SAFETY AND EFFECTIVENESS OF CIPROFLOXACIN IN CHILDREN, ADOLESCENTS (LESS THAN 18 YEARS OF AGE), PREGNANT WOMEN, AND LACTATING WOMEN HAVE NOT BEEN ESTABLISHED.**

**MILES**
Pharmaceutical Division

Miles Inc.
Pharmaceutical Division
400 Morgan Lane
West Haven, CT 06516

© May 1992, Miles Inc. Pharmaceutical Division    Printed in U.S.A.    CO9422

cause that's the best result for them and their families and their employers, but because it's best for doctors. But we have to be reeducated to understand even the indirect ramifications of our decisions. If we make decisions in a vacuum and don't fully consider the impact they have on a person's ability to work or to stay active, we're missing a great element of the healing process.

*You've mentioned that health care in the 21st century is evolving into measured care. Please explain.*

Basically, you can't manage what you don't measure. To measure care, you've got to have an information system that accounts for what happens clinically as much as what happens financially.

The traditional models of managed care in the 1980s were reactive, meaning they tried to control interventions and treatment costs after an illness by using a gatekeeper system. But trying to manage costs that way merely leads to cost shifting, as care is restricted or deferred by reduced coverage in benefit plans. The models of the 1990s and beyond will need to emphasize prevention. That's going to take cooperation we don't normally see from health teams. It means that the primary-care doctor will have to move beyond gatekeeper to healthkeeper. It also means measuring differences between individual providers, treatment programs, and integrated health systems to find the best practices and feeding the results back to the providers.

*Isn't that what managed-care organizations are doing now?*

To some degree. However, they have focused on a retrospective review of trends. We have tracked data before, but never to monitor processes and outcomes of care as they occur.

*Is the emphasis on measured care something doctors should fear?*

It's a big shift in the way we think, but it should be incredibly empowering if we do it right. We can develop the clinical guidelines; we can create the clinical decision-making support systems; we can better measure and interpret the outcomes of care so that we can truly manage the services we provide.

*Are you suggesting a system to weed out problem doctors?*

Not at all. No one is proposing that we start looking around for bad apples—the old way of doing quality assurance. But if we know the best practice parameters and apply them in our own practices, we can be accountable for improving the quality of care.

*What does the application of business practices to health care mean for individual physicians?*

For the practicing doctor, the only question is how we're going to apply these changes. They will occur—as they have already. And that means we have to accustom ourselves to being part of a bigger organized system of care, whether it's a group practice, an integrated health care delivery system, or an HMO. We'll also have to focus on health care as a system, not just independent episodes of care with individual patients. Health care is going to be a continuum of care, not only for our patients but for the population at large.

*What would you say to a doctor who is undecided about participating in a managed-care organization?*

Be selective about your entry point but then jump in. The time to get involved is now, when we can still affect policy. Those who think they don't like managed care are responding to the word *managed*. They think of management as something external like utilization review, dialing 1-800-MAY-I to an organization a thousand miles away. But what we have to do internally is demonstrate to ourselves, our patients, and our health care purchasers that our decisions are medically appropriate and that we're accountable.

Many of us are going to feel better about our practices knowing that we're doing the right thing in the right way at the right time, and we'll have ways of measuring that. Now we're paid for how much we do, not whether it was the right thing to do.

Under managed care we'll be able to use the best resources for those who really need them. We won't have to use what's left over of a limited resource that could have been used more efficiently. A lot of doctors will find that reallocation exciting.

*How do doctors respond when you talk with them about managed care?*

Most physicians recognize these trends. They know they need to get involved, but many don't know how. They're looking for some education, some framework or context that sensibly links these elements. They want to know how managed care works in a clinical setting because they want to position themselves in the marketplace. Usually the leaders of a large group practice are already familiar with the issues. The challenge is to prepare the group.

*What role do you expect communication skills to play in the new models of health care?*

Improved communication will play a key role. The medical community will soon have access to a vast communication highway. Individual physicians will be able to hook up electronically with data repositories to get information leading to the best care for their patients. Right now the majority of management systems and computer systems record financial transactions. But clinical transactions should be the focus.

And patients are getting more sophisticated about demanding information. It used to be, "Trust me, I'm your doctor." Now I'm hearing, "Show me, I'm your patient." Sometimes results of research appear in *The Wall Street Journal* before the medical journals; patients often read about things before doctors do. But that will change as we set up telecommunication networks that give us access to updated information on the best treatment for a particular patient.

*What about communication on another level: the old-fashioned kind between doctor and patient, or doctor and doctor?*

For practicing physicians, the changes in the delivery of health care entail enhancing some skills they already have and learning new ones, and I'm convinced the one skill we need to pay attention to is communication—between physician and patient, among physicians, and from physician to managed-care organization. We've got to be able to explain the relative risks and benefits of procedures, tests, and medical decisions to patients as well as to employers. We've also got to listen well.

*Isn't that inherent in what doctors already do?*

Yes, but the issues are going to be much more complicated and elaborate. For one thing, we're going to have to demonstrate to the patient as well as the insurer or employer that what we're doing is appropriate, necessary, and cost-efficient. In fully capitated managed-care systems we will want to demonstrate those qualities to ourselves, because we will be at risk financially. We've always made decisions based on what we thought was best for the patient. We have to continue to do that, but also consider cost.

*But you're still faced with patients who may want more care than the doctors think is necessary.*

That's right, especially because patients are the ultimate drivers of care and often come with expectations that determine how the physician responds. No matter how conscientious a doctor is, the patient can still say, "Well, when my neighbor had a headache, she got an MRI, and I want an MRI for my headache as well." Doctors are going to have to deal with a chasm of expectations between patient desires and economic pressures. Once again, the decisions will have to come out of the gut-level communication between the physician and the patient.

# CHAPTER three

# HUMANIZING THE HMO

For almost five years, internist Francine Gaillour was happy in a 12-doctor private practice outside Seattle. She was a top revenue producer and a full partner. "The practice was my baby," she said. But when she decided to have a child and wanted to work part time, the other partners vetoed the idea. Soon she was talking to Group Health Cooperative of Puget Sound, one of the country's oldest and largest staff-model HMOs, about sharing a practice with another doctor.

She made the move, though not without grave reservations about finding her niche there. "I was worried that I was just going to be doctor number 839 out of many, many doctors, and I didn't like that idea at all." Four years later the 39-year-old mother of two has learned not only how to handle the frustrations of managed care within a large system, but also how to effect changes. And Gaillour has been deeply impressed by the quality of care at the cooperative—an unexpected bonus, she said.

Still, she remains ambivalent about her role at the HMO. Some things she had taken for granted in her practice were alien to the group members, most of whom had never worked for themselves. According to Gaillour, the real impediment to change is not nameless bureaucrats or the system, but doctors who sit on the sidelines. Individual doctors can and should assert themselves, she said.

*Dr. Francine R. Gaillour*
*Internist*

*Tell me about your transition to managed care. How difficult has it been for you?*

DR. GAILLOUR: It was a huge blow at first. I had joined a well-established practice in Kirkland, a suburb of Seattle, and I had a wonderful group of patients. I was the first woman the group hired. And after the first year as one of its top revenue producers, I became a full partner.

When I got pregnant with my first child, I decided to work part time. But the other doctors resisted; they didn't want any part-time partners. I went through a real crisis when I decided to leave.

I talked with a doctor who had been working at Group Health part time for several years. She told me that they were very supportive of doctors cutting their hours to spend time with their families. I decided I wanted to try, and I joined in 1990.

I have to admit that the first year at Group Health, I was depressed. I could see how much less autonomy I had as an employee at a big HMO than in private practice, where I made my own hours. That was the adjustment that hit me hardest.

*Did your pay suffer?*

No. As a matter of fact, one thing that I really like about working at an HMO is the way I'm paid. If I were in private practice and I worked four days a week, my earnings the first three days would just pay overhead. At Group Health, I share a panel of 1,800 patients with another doctor. We each work two and a half days a week and together we make up a full practice. That means I get paid exactly half of one salary, plus full benefits.

*Did you find working for an HMO different than you expected?*

I don't know that it was different; I didn't know much about Group Health before I joined. But I did feel like I was taking a step down in joining a big co-op. For one thing, I was used to spending more time with my patients. My first week of work, when I learned that I was supposed to perform physical exams in 30 minutes, I rebelled. I told the receptionist, "I need 45 minutes to do a physical exam. I can't do one in half an hour." I believed that I'd have to leave something out. Within two hours the clinic chief was in my office to give me the official line: "This is the way we do it here. This is just the way it's done." I know he was well-meaning. He thought if we changed the schedule we wouldn't be able to see as many patients, and it would disrupt patient care or make our waiting time longer. I understood that, but it was still frustrating.

*How have you resolved the issue?*

I do a "health screening exam," which is an abbreviated physical tailored to patients according to their age, sex, health risk factors, and ongoing medical problems. It simply isn't necessary to look into everyone's mouth and ears once a year. I have designed my own physical exam form as well to say "interval health screening" and not "complete physical." I do have some concern about liability when I am put in this position by the co-op of being expected to do a lot of screening exams too quickly. And I still have to meet the patients' expectations of a "yearly physical." So I spend a fair amount of time educating patients about what they really need.

*Have your feelings about the cooperative changed?*

Very much. After almost four years, I'm convinced I made the right decision. For one thing, Group Health is an excellent facility. We provide first-rate care. I'd even say the *overall* level of quality is as high as or higher than in private practice, primarily because care is so well integrated both in terms of specialties and ancillary services such as pharmacy, nursing, and social services.

*How has your relationship to your patients changed?*

It can still be too impersonal. When I was in private practice, I would go into the exam room and meet the patient and do the interview. Then I'd leave the room, let the patient undress, and go back in to do the exam. At Group Health, the first time I meet patients, they're in their gowns—completely naked under their gowns, meeting their doctor. That's not the way I like to treat people. And yet that is the way it's done, in the name of efficiency.

Then, too, most of my new patients come to me without knowing much about me, and that's more impersonal as well. In private practice, patients came to me by word of mouth. They'd heard good things from another patient. At an HMO, they pick a doctor based on who's available and whose picture they like.

*Do you feel that you're not treating your patients as well as you would like?*

Not really. In fact, I've learned a different attitude about what constitutes the best care. I've come to see that managed care in many ways allows me to practice medicine better, and more ethically.

When I was in private practice, for example, I devised a health-maintenance calendar that told my patients exactly when they needed to come in for their Pap smears, physicals, prostate checks, and mammograms—a nice little marketing device. At the time I believed that everyone should have a yearly physical. But after a while I realized there was no evidence that yearly physicals keep people healthier. They're simply built into the American system like apple pie.

What's more, in private practice physical exams are not covered by insurance. So many doctors do a bit of creative diagnosing, writing down something like menstrual disorder or fatigue so the patients' insurance will cover the cost. If patients have to pay out of pocket you might never see them again—or at least not as often.

In managed care, the arrangement is the opposite. Physical exams and preventive medicine are covered, so an avalanche of patients want to come in for physical exams every year. My partner calculated that because our practice is 80 percent female, it would take a year just to get through all the Pap smears, performing seven or eight a day.

*Have you had to discourage people from getting physicals or Pap smears?*

Well, we've been able to educate our patients that there are only a few specific screening interventions that actually reduce mortality. The research shows that healthy, asymptomatic women who have had two or three consecutive normal Pap smears only need screenings every two years or so, and they don't benefit from a complete physical exam at all. It makes more sense for us to do a physical if a patient comes in with a problem.

When I manage patients' care this way, I'm truer to myself and to the medical profession because I'm not giving people excess care. At an HMO I don't get paid any more for doing 10 physicals than I would for doing one. There's no incentive to bring people in needlessly. But I admit I still do a lot of unnecessary screening, blood testing, and chest X-rays on healthy people because old habits die hard and also because I have an underlying fear of being sued for not detecting someone's occult esoteric cancer on their routine annual.

*Aren't your observations about excess care true of private practice as well?*

Of course, in private practice you don't believe you're giving your patients excess care. But a part of you always knows you need to build your practice. You want patients to come in for any little thing. Every time you order a chest X-ray or mammogram in your clinic, you get credit for it. And even if you think that's not influencing you, it can never be too far from the back of your mind.

*You mentioned loss of autonomy. Can you expand on that?*

In private practice I was my own boss. If I wanted to have a two-hour lunch and nobody was scheduled, I could. It was my schedule and nobody said a thing. Of course if you don't see patients you don't make money—which means that you don't end up doing those two-hour lunches very often.

My greatest fear about the HMO was that some faceless, bureaucratic number-cruncher would tell me how to practice medicine—all in the name of keeping costs down. And there have been many times when I've felt like I was banging my head against a wall because something I'd considered routine in private practice required so much energy to do at Group Health. But the surprising thing has been that the "wall" isn't some mysterious administrator in some faraway office. The wall is some of the doctors I work with—particularly those who've never worked in private practice. Many don't realize that they do have the freedom to do things their own way. I feel sorry for some of them because they have such an employee mentality. They get entrenched in the way they think things have to be done. It's as if they imagine some invisible person is looking over their shoulder all the time.

My colleagues are all talented physicians with the best intentions, but they think change requires some sort of committee or something more complicated than simply saying, "Let's just change it."

*When you joined Group Health, what added skills did you need?*

Other than expanding my knowledge of pediatric care, I don't think I had to learn any new medical skills. About 50 percent of the internists here don't see children or adolescents. And I wanted to because I'd already had some exposure to them in my practice, my partner saw kids, and I was about to have a baby. I felt like I could learn to do it. But that was only a small amount of knowledge to add to my base. Overall I am probably using fewer of my skills in internal medicine because of the way the co-op is organized and the way they use internists. But if I had said, "Listen, I don't want to see kids at all," that would have been fine.

*So you are using fewer skills?*

Using fewer internal medicine skills. I could be saving many referrals to specialists, such as cardiologists or gastroenterologists. As an internist I could handle many people with chest pain, I could do treadmill tests, bone-marrow biopsies, I could do a lot of non-invasive gastroenterology, yet family doctors don't refer to me or any general internists because they're so used to referring to specialists. The internal medicine subspecialists know that they are relatively overstaffed and that it wouldn't be in their best interest to send work my way. But the situation is not unique to Group Health.

*What nonmedical skills have you had to learn?*

I don't know if skill is the right word. The name of the game when you're practicing is seeing patients, 90 percent of the time, or doing patient care in some form or another; the other 10 percent of the time you spend adjusting or grumbling. Tolerance, maybe that is a skill. Patience, yes. It probably took me three years to adjust to the policies here and to some of the doctors' views.

*How much of a difference can one doctor make in an organization like Group Health? Can you give me an example?*

In my first six months, I realized that we were booked solid with appointments every morning. Our patients were getting upset because if they got sick, we had no time to fit them in that day. And if we did, everyone was incredibly overworked and the wait times for routine appointments were much too long. The schedule was creating havoc. It was mind-boggling to me that no one even questioned it. I didn't want to stand for it. So I said, "I can't do a good job when I'm rushing. I don't want to make mistakes with documentation, with prescriptions, in diagnosis."

In private practice I had my medical reference books behind me, and I was looking things up all day so that I could learn as I practiced. But at Group Health I felt like I was being rushed through an assembly line. I said, "We're seeing too many patients." And one of the doctors turned to me and said, "You know, I don't think I've ever heard anyone come out and say that." But it was the truth. And the thing was, I wasn't the only one who felt that way. All the doctors were feeling terrible that they weren't able to cater to patients the way they wanted to.

*What did you do?*

The solution was pretty obvious. It was just a matter of saying, "We're going to back off. We're not going to book as many patients." We would leave about seven appointments open each day to fit people in. It was such a simple idea. And yet it went against the grain of the way things were done. My own clinic chief was the most resistant, and we had many arguments. After that I realized that the doctors themselves needed to be enlightened. We weren't dealing with anonymous widget-counters in some central office.

*How did the doctor who shares your practice respond to your crusade?*

She and I struggled over it. I told her the schedule was ridiculous and that it worked against our strengths as doctors. But it took about six months to convince her. That was definitely a skill I needed to learn: how to talk to people and persuade them that we are grown-ups, we can handle our schedule, and we can control our patient flow.

*You were able to bring about the change. How has it worked out?*

Initially, I felt I had a much better handle on my schedule and my day. I had enough time to do better documentation. Basically, I knew from my private practice what my optimum number of patients was. If I exceeded that I would become stressed and that would affect how I interacted with patients and staff and how well I thought I was performing. Anybody can move a huge number of patients through their clinic, but that's not what I take pride in.

So once I had better control of my schedule, I did feel that patients were seen appropriately; that is, the acutely ill were seen promptly and patients needing elective screening exams scheduled appointments for a later date.

The bad news is, we are currently so short-staffed at our primary-care clinic that there is no safety net for the overflow of patients who need to be seen immediately. That means that if I have seven appointment times set aside and 15 patients need to come in, that's too bad for me. I'm skipping lunch and staying late, and feeling that patients are probably not getting proper medical care. And patients get the idea that access is a problem, and they resent it.

*It sounds as though the skills you developed as a private practitioner have been of real benefit.*

That's right. The whole issue seemed so logical to me because in the world of private practice, you roll out the red carpet for patients. But at Group Health people don't have that concept—that you must retain your patients, that the customer is always right. That mentality is new.

*But doesn't Group Health's accommodation show some flexibility?*

It does. And the grass isn't much greener in private practice these days. All doctors have to deal with bureaucracy. In my case I had to deal with partners who didn't want a part-time doctor in their practice. I did not feel great being a trailblazer there. But at Group Health it's quite common for even men to be sharing practices. Group Health has turned out to be a lot more accommodating.

*What's your role in the cooperative's gatekeeper system?*

I hate the phrase *gatekeeper*. I function as a primary-care physician, managing 80 percent of the problems for 80 percent of the patients. If patients want to see a specialist for problems that can be handled by me or any other primary-care provider, that is still their right, in this organization. That happens occasionally and I try not to take it personally or to resist it. I don't encourage it, though. I don't like being used just to do triage.

*What's wrong with those patients seeing a specialist? Isn't he or she better equipped to deal with specific problems?*

In some cases, yes. But many times a patient gets referred just to keep things moving—even when a primary-care physician could have dealt with the problem just fine. Many family doctors are so overwhelmed by the large volume of patients and the amount of new research and new medications coming out that they end up doing simple triage. When they see a patient with a semicomplex problem, they don't think, *How can I evaluate this?* They think, *Who shall I refer this to?* That is part of the mentality that's been feeding these specialists.

Let's say a patient has an elevated thyroid-function test. That is the sort of medical problem that many internists find interesting. When I started at Group Health, my partner was referring those problems to an endocrinologist. I said, "Give me all the general internal medicine cases." So now the only internal medicine cases we refer are those who need a procedure like a colonoscopy or a treadmill test or those I have done some workups on already. I could do treadmills and other noninvasive cardiology, but the clinic is relatively overstaffed with cardiologists so we do refer those.

*You were successful in getting the co-op to change its scheduling patterns. Any success on this front?*

I have been trying for three and a half years to find a niche where I can do more general consultative medicine in the co-op, but I've given up on that idea. There is no incentive on the part of family practitioners or subspecialists to encourage the use of an internist. That's one issue—the demise of the general internist—that I have been struggling with and trying to make peace with since I joined the co-op. I saw it coming in private practice, but here because the practice structures are so rigid I feel the loss and disappointment more acutely.

*How do you feel about the difference in pay for family practitioners and specialists?*

It really upsets me, and the inequity is across the board, not just at Group Health. One of the things I've become most involved in here is trying to compensate physicians for their cognitive skills.

Currently there is a two-tiered salary system both in private practice and in HMOs. For the last 20 years physicians who do procedures—especially those based in hospitals—have been paid a great deal more than physicians who use cognitive skills.

As an internist, for example, I might spend 45 minutes with a diabetic patient who has acute pneumonia, a new atrial fibrillation, and a possible heart attack. Yet I would make more money sewing up a three-centimeter laceration than I could managing all of those problems. Every time a specialist uses new machinery for imaging or ablating or scoping, there is a premium attached to it out of proportion to the cognitive skills necessary for diagnosis. And the vast number of those diagnoses are made by primary-care doctors.

I once read a quote from an orthopod who said that his services were highly valued because he could take someone with an arthritic hip and make him walk again. But by gosh an internist can take a patient in a diabetic ketoacidosis coma and make him walk again. Procedures pay. That's why primary-care doctors make less than $100,000 a year while surgeons make well over $300,000.

*Doesn't Group Health have to pay what the market will bear?*

The problem is that it is basing salaries on a model that's no longer viable. In fee-for-service medicine, specialists could demand the sort of money they've been getting. But the situation is radically different now. There are way too many specialists. Hospital closures and cutbacks also affect the need for specialists. You see anesthesiologists running around like crazy trying to find positions. But turn to any medical society publication and you find two pages of ads for primary-care physicians. The market is crying out for them. It just needs to compensate them better.

*What will it take to drive up salaries?*

You can see it happening already. In the Northwest, for example, large specialty hospital groups are frantically courting big primary-care groups. Obviously there's going to be some transfer of revenue. I know of one doctor recruited by a hospital as an independent contractor who is paid a salary 50 percent higher than mine. So the folks who have the money are willing to pay the price.

I'd love to see Group Health be the innovator. We're one of the five largest medical groups in the country. I'd like us to be in the headlines: "Hey, look at Group Health. They're about to dismantle the salary schedule for something fair and equitable."

*How much support do you have among your fellow doctors?*

It's interesting. I just sent a letter out to the co-op doctors in which I basically explained what I've just told you. I mentioned that the current inequity comes about as a result of the fee-for-service model of medical practice. But it simply doesn't make sense for HMOs to base their salaries on what people get paid in private practice. That letter ruffled some feathers, let me tell you. The reason I'm excited, though, is not so much the money issue. If I wanted to make more money, I'd work full time. To me it's an equity issue. I see my profession, general internal medicine, being squeezed out because so many specialists—gastroenterologists and cardiologists—need to justify their own positions. But you can't disenfranchise a third of your doctors just so that you can enrich the other two-thirds.

*Your call to arms comes at a good time, when almost everyone is calling for more generalists. Are you encouraged?*

It's true that the government is trying to encourage more doctors to go into primary-care medicine, which is important. But for that to happen, salaries are going to have to go up significantly. Some have proposed passing legislation that would force medical schools to turn out more primary-care doctors and limit the funding for subspecialties. My point, to borrow a phrase from the Clinton campaign, is, "It's the money, stupid." Once you start paying family doctors $150,000 to $200,000 a year, there won't be a problem.

The only way to accomplish that is through capitation, where the doctors figure out how they're going to divide the money up, rather than assuming that if they have an ophthalmologist on staff they have to pay him or her $300,000 a year. I want people to understand that primary-care doctors should be paid more not because there's a shortage, even though that's one reason that things will be changing, but because it's the fair thing to do.

*"As some men get drunk on alcohol,
so he gets drunk on science."*
—Leo Tolstoy

Miles is proud to present this series on...

# Powerful Innovators

# Powerful Innovator

*Elie Metchnikoff (1845-1916)*

*With a flash of inspiration, Elie Metchnikoff broadened our understanding of the immune system.*

*While observing the mobile cells of transparent starfish larvae, he suddenly wondered if "similar cells might help defend the organism against intruders."*

*Thus was born his controversial "phagocyte" (derived from the Greek, meaning "devouring cell") theory. His notion that white blood cells digest bacteria was denounced by many scientists. But Metchnikoff impressed Louis Pasteur, who invited the Russian microbiologist to join the Pasteur Institute in 1888.*

*An emotional man, given to wild hypotheses, Metchnikoff apparently ran his lab like a three-ring circus. Despite his unorthodox style, Metchnikoff's work in immunology was recognized, and earned him the Nobel Prize in Physiology or Medicine in 1908, an honor he shared with immunologist Paul Ehrlich.*

# Powerful Antimicrobial

*No other fluoroquinolone is more active* in vitro *against* Enterobacteriaceae *and* Pseudomonas aeruginosa *than ciprofloxacin.*[1]* *Comparing MIC$_{90s}$, ciprofloxacin is 8 times more active against* P aeruginosa *than ofloxacin or lomefloxacin.*[1]* *Moreover, a nationwide surveillance study found that ≥98% of* Enterobacter *species were susceptible or moderately susceptible† to ciprofloxacin.*[2]*

*The most potent fluoroquinolone.*[1,3,4]*

# Powerful Numbers

*speak for themselves:*

**99**...*Percent isolates of* **Enterobacter cloacae** *(n=5,170) that were susceptible or moderately susceptible[†] to ciprofloxacin in a recent nationwide surveillance survey.*[2*]

**98**...*Percent isolates of* **E coli** *(n=28,805) that were susceptible or moderately susceptible[†] to ciprofloxacin in a recent nationwide surveillance survey.*[2*]

**97**...*Percent isolates of* **K pneumoniae** *(n=9,774) that were susceptible or moderately susceptible[†] to ciprofloxacin in a recent nationwide surveillance survey.*[2*]

**Cipro® I.V.**
(ciprofloxacin)

*The most potent fluoroquinolone.*[1,3,4*]

[*]*In vitro* activity does not necessarily imply a correlation with *in vivo* results.

[†]Susceptible defined as an $MIC_{90} \leq 1$ μg/mL; moderately susceptible defined as $MIC_{90} = 2$ μg/mL. Survey data collected from 25 centers in 21 states from 1990 to 1991.

*Please see complete prescribing information and cited references at the end of this book.*

**MILES**
**Pharmaceutical Division**

Miles Inc.
Pharmaceutical Division
400 Morgan Lane
West Haven, CT 06516

# CHAPTER four

# THE PAYER'S PERSPECTIVE

T wenty-four years as a small town family practitioner did not dent Dr. Ross Egger's enthusiasm for private practice. He was tired, however, of the frustrations of dealing with insurance companies and had lots of ideas about how they could do things better. He served as a committee adviser for Blue Cross and Blue Shield of Indiana, and in 1985, when the insurer needed a full-time medical director, it turned to Egger. At first he said no. But a tragic malpractice suit and the urgings of his wife made him decide to accept the challenge.

Six years later Egger, 56, had a new perspective on managed care. Developing efficiency standards and protocols and recruiting doctors had persuaded him that most of the people directing managed care are, like him, doctors who want to create the fairest and most scientifically accurate means of improving care. He had also learned that sound management can occur only when physicians participate in making the decisions that affect how they practice.

He had discovered, too, that he missed working directly with patients. In 1991 the Indiana native returned to small-town practice in Middletown, Indiana, this time in partnership with a hospital that wanted to become more involved with managed care. He brought to the practice his relatively new conviction that managed care can deliver doctors from the administrative hassles of medicine.

*Dr. Ross L. Egger*
*Family Practitioner*

And he learned that for doctors who have always practiced cost-efficient medicine, who have thought about both quality and cost, the transition to managed care can be painless.

*Why did you leave private practice ?*

DR. EGGER: I had been in practice for 22 years when I had my first and only malpractice suit. At the time I didn't think it had affected me much, but I've come to realize that it must have. A couple in their twenties to whom I was very close called me about three times around Christmas 1984. The husband was vomiting. I told them to meet me at the emergency room, but for whatever reason, they wouldn't do it. By the time they did, he had a ruptured appendix. The young man died. I think the surgeon really messed up by telling the wife that if he had gotten a call sooner, her husband wouldn't have died.

The young man was a fine, fine person, and I felt terrible about his death. In fact, I'm glad the wife sued because she needed some money to raise their kids. In Indiana a review board of doctors and lawyers meets to look your case over. They concluded that I was negligent because I hadn't forced the patient to come to the hospital and that the patient was negligent because he hadn't come to the hospital—something I'd never heard of. They asked me if I wanted to contest the decision. The suit was for only $100,000, and I told them no, the family needed the money. I hadn't done anything wrong, but being sued did smart, especially after I'd spent so much time working with this couple and was so fond of them.

I was serving at the time on an advisory committee for Blue Cross and Blue Shield and noticed that it lacked necessary information and data. I would go to an evening committee meeting once a month and show them ways to improve. One day they called me and said, "We've decided to hire a full-time medical director. Would you be interested?"

"Absolutely not," I told them.

"We'll pay you good money; we'll give you retirement; you'll have no more night calls."

When my wife heard that, she did a double flip. "Let's do it," she said. So I did. I thought it might be a nice challenge, and coming so soon after that young man's death, I thought I might like to do something else.

One of my tasks was to help Blue Cross start a statewide preferred-provider organization. It had just gotten state approval; I had to explain the PPO to all the hospital staffs and county medical societies and to set up and publish the necessary guidelines.

*What were your concerns about helping Blue Cross start a PPO?*

When PPOs first started, many accepted guidelines developed

by academicians. The guidelines drove physicians up the wall because they couldn't see the logic behind them. They had formulas like this: A person with blood in his urine can be seen four times; if he is seen a fifth time, the payer should challenge that visit. But the number of visits was arbitrary.

What I told Indiana physicians was that Blue Cross and Blue Shield had given me the freedom to put together a set of guidelines that would not alienate doctors, as long as they were cost-effective for Blue Cross. That's what I tried hardest to do: create guidelines that said for this specific disease, this specific case, this doctor did the right thing. And I wanted the guidelines to be based on doctors' real-life experiences. I always felt that if a decision was not medically logical, if I couldn't back it up with the medical literature or the experience that I or others have had, then my decision was wrong.

When issues got touchy—such as when to approve a CAT scan or an MRI—I'd call a meeting of a specialty society to discuss the problems and to develop appropriate criteria. I reviewed what was available from other companies, and we compiled manuals to use for recertification, retrospective review, and quality auditing.

I took as many Blue Cross decisions as I could out to the doctors. I'd sit with a panel of radiologists and say, "All right, if you don't like my decision, tell me a better one." Sometimes I talked to as many as 100 doctors in a single staff meeting, most of whom saw me as the enemy. I felt like Daniel going into the lions' den, but I understood exactly what the doctors were concerned about.

The majority of doctors accepted the guidelines we came up with. And other Blue Cross plans began using them as well. The key was that we involved physicians. The guidelines weren't pulled out of the sky.

*As you traveled the state, what did you find out about doctors' expectations and fears?*

Their biggest fear is that somebody will interfere with the way they practice medicine. I think all physicians have a deep-down fear that the way they do things may not be the best way. Doctors talk, we watch movies or filmstrips or hear lectures on different topics, but we don't ever see firsthand how others practice medicine. If people are looking over our shoulders, we're afraid they're going to say, "Hey, I found you doing something really wrong, and I'm going to tell somebody."

I've had to allay that fear in myself, to realize that there are many ways of doing things, and nobody is about to say that there is only one way and that's the way you're going to have to do it. We certainly didn't do that at Blue Cross and Blue Shield while I was medical director. We always made it clear that what was important was the outcome.

Sometimes a managed-care organization does say, "You may have used that successfully for years, but our data show that it just isn't as effective as such-and-such." What I do then is look at the data. If I agree I'll thank the organization for recommending an improvement; I won't consider it an affront. In fact, I'm convinced most doctors who involve themselves in managed care end up doing better medicine than they did before. If a doctor gives a recommendation thoughtful consideration and still doesn't agree, he can say so.

*Is the doctors' fear of interference unjustified?*

Most managed-care plans are run by doctors similar to myself, who have tried extremely hard to be fair and to be certain that every decision they make is backed up by hard science. But the plans do have to think about alleviating that fear. They have to let doctors know that the organization is not going to tell them how to practice medicine nor blow the whistle if they practice differently from their peers.

*Some physicians express strong reservations about losing their freedom to choose patients. Are there grounds for such worries?*

Yes and no. It's true that a lot of doctors are afraid that managed-care organizations will dump them with a bunch of patients they don't like—patients other doctors don't want. But there are ways of asking a patient to find another physician, even in managed care, especially a patient who doesn't cooperate with you.

*You seem more at ease with managed care than most doctors. Is that because of your experience with Blue Cross and Blue Shield?*

Yes. Before getting the job, I was always calling Blue Cross to complain about some of its policies. I'd ask, "Where is that SOB director?" And he was never there, because Blue Cross didn't have a full-time medical director. After I became the director, whenever I spoke to hospital staffs or county medical societies, I'd introduce myself as that SOB that I had been trying to contact for 10 years.

So, yes, I realized that I was now representing a different side of managed care. It was my job to convince doctors there was nothing to be afraid of and that a physician practicing good, reasonable medicine would have no problems whatsoever.

*Are there new skills that physicians will need under managed care?*

You do hear a lot about new skills, but that's nonsense. A doctor going into managed care needs only one skill: he has to be able to justify what he does. That's it. For years physicians never had to justify any medical procedure. If I ordered a $10,000 test, nobody questioned it—unless the patient had to pay for it, and then he or she might object. But patients rarely questioned such tests because their insurance paid. Under managed care, all that changes. A doctor has to ask himself, "Does the patient really need this test?"

*In other words, each doctor needs to be more cost-effective.*

Exactly right. But he should have been cost-effective from the beginning. If he's not already, he will have a lot of learning to do and probably have a lot of trouble changing. Perhaps he has trouble communicating with his patients. He might not be comfortable telling a worried parent, "I don't think your son needs a skull X-ray just because he got hit with a baseball." Some doctors would avoid the conflict and simply order the X-ray. Or if a patient asks, "But do I really need such a test?" the doctor might respond, "Who are you to question me?" A lot of physicians practice that way. They'll have to change.

*What made you a cost-efficient doctor?*

It just came naturally. I didn't know a thing about medicine when I went into it. My dad was an electrician, and I didn't have any role models in medicine. When I started practicing, I did what I thought was logical, and I learned to work with people. We developed diagnoses together. I still do it that way. And I have trained the residents I've worked with to do that too.

I started practicing back before insurance paid so well. Only half of my patients had insurance, and most of those had a pretty small amount. So if you did an X-ray, you had to justify it. You had to say, this skull film is going to cost you 35 bucks, but I think it's necessary. I wouldn't do anything that I thought patients couldn't afford unless I really felt they needed it. And I'd sit down and spend 15 minutes explaining why they did. Doctors don't do that now, but I learned to be cost-effective by practicing that way.

*Do you think managed care helps doctors become more efficient?*

Absolutely. And I think managed care for a physician who already practices good, sound, cost-effective health care is a breeze. He doesn't have to do anything different.

Plenty of things reveal a doctor's effectiveness. Unfortunately, most haven't been explored. How many patients does the doctor see per hour? What is his hospitalization rate? If he sees patients superficially, he won't take care of the sick ones properly and will have to hospitalize more. How often does he see a patient on a return visit? If you review those issues as well as the doctor's referral and prescription habits, you'll get a good idea of his effectiveness.

*Why did you decide to leave management for a private-practice arrangement with St. John's Hospital?*

To tell the truth, I had been bored doing management work. And my vanity caught up with me: I missed the immediate gratification I got from patients. The only thank-you you ever got at Blue Cross was a bonus at the end of the year. No one would call you on the phone to say, "Man, I want to thank you for preventing that lawsuit." That just doesn't happen in the corporate world. Yet in family practice I used to get those thank-yous every 15 minutes.

*Your arrangement with St. John's sounds like an embryonic physician-hospital organization. Would you describe it?*

I joined St. John's after five years with Blue Cross and after one year of helping Prudential form an HMO in Cincinnati. I happened to be home in Middletown for a vacation when a guy from St. John's called to ask if I'd ever thought about going back into practice. The hospital offered to set me up. It would rent an office, hire whatever office staff I needed, and pay me a salary; anything I made over the cost of the practice, we would split. We've been in that arrangement since 1991.

*What do you get out of such a setup?*

That's easy. I can do what I enjoy best—treat patients—without the administrative hassle of running a private practice. I don't have to worry about collections or supplies or any of that stuff.

*And the hospital?*

The hospital makes money each time I request lab work or X-rays. On any given day, I may request a dozen lab procedures, four or five X-rays, or a $1,000 MRI. That money goes to the hospital.

More important, the hospital hopes to increase its base of patients. St. John's felt that patients from Middletown were migrating toward Muncie, where a larger competitor, Ball Memorial Hospital, is. St. John's thought that if I was set up with my own office in Middletown, I'd refer patients who needed hospital services to St. John's. But I don't have to admit patients there. I'm listed as a member of two PPOs and three or four HMOs. I can admit patients wherever I have privileges. And I do.

*Isn't the motivation of St. John's to get all your referrals?*

We talked about that. Several people who live in Middletown wanted to be my patients but belong to an HMO affiliated with Ball. So I approached St. John's and said, "Why don't I also join the staff at Ball? If I could see these patients for routine office visits, they would be paying St. John's in effect. In the rare instances when I have to put them in Ball, that wouldn't cost St. John's anything." St. John's agreed.

*What percentage of doctors in your area belong to a managed-care organization?*

The Anderson-Muncie community was the last one in Indiana to have active PPOs and HMOs, so few physicians participate in

*"As long as I have a water tap, a flame, and some blotting paper, I can just as well work in a barn."*

Miles is proud to present this series on...

# Powerful Innovators

# Powerful Physician

*Paul Ehrlich (1854-1915)*

Even as a child, Ehrlich displayed the curiosity and imagination we associate with brilliant scientists. His vivid descriptions earned him the nickname "Dr. Fantasy."

Ehrlich proved a gifted, intuitive experimenter who astonished his colleagues with the accuracy of his work.

In 1908, Ehrlich was awarded a share of the Nobel Prize in medicine and physiology for his research on immunity and serum. He spent the better part of two decades studying chemicals to find those that would selectively kill bacteria without harming humans. Interestingly, his most famous discovery came after he won the Nobel Prize, when he identified a compound known as "606"—naming it Salvasan (from salvation)—and identified its usefulness against syphilis—one of the most feared, albeit least discussed, diseases at that time.

Ehrlich's work marked the beginning of modern chemotherapy. Many believe that he set in motion the quick discovery of cures for many infectious diseases.

# Powerful Antimicrobial

Today, in lower respiratory infections,* some pathogens are no longer routinely susceptible to traditional agents. One important reason the power of Cipro® stands out is its unique mode of action. It allows the power of Cipro® to remain unaffected by ß-lactamase or plasmid-mediated resistance. And cross-resistance, which often limits the usefulness of other classes of antibiotics, is not a problem reported with Cipro®. In fact, Cipro® kills susceptible pathogens* during all four phases of cell growth.[†]

**Cipro®** TABLETS

*(ciprofloxacin HCl)*

## The most potent fluoroquinolone.[1-3‡]

*Due to susceptible strains of indicated pathogens. See indicated organisms in prescribing information.
[†]Data on file, Miles Inc Pharmaceutical Division.
[‡]*In vitro* activity does not necessarily imply a correlation with *in vivo* results.

*See full prescribing information at the end of this book.*

# Powerful Numbers

*Speak for themselves*

**12** ...*The number of hours serum concentrations of Cipro® are maintained in excess of MIC$_{90}$s of most susceptible bacteria.*

**96** ...*The percentage of favorable clinical response (resolution + improvement) with Cipro® in lower respiratory infections due to susceptible strains of indicated pathogens.*

**250/500/750** ...*Dosage strengths of Cipro® Tablets available.*

**Cipro®** TABLETS

(ciprofloxacin HCl)

The most potent fluoroquinolone.[1-3‡]

**CIPRO® SHOULD NOT BE USED IN CHILDREN, ADOLESCENTS, OR PREGNANT WOMEN.**

*See full prescribing information at the end of this book.*

Pharmaceutical Division

Miles Inc.
Pharmaceutical Division
400 Morgan Lane
West Haven, CT 06516

© April 1991, Miles Inc. Pharmaceutical Division    Printed in U.S.A.    CO9651

managed care. But it is growing, especially because most doctors in Indiana have not had bad experiences with HMOs. We haven't had any horror stories like those we've read about in Florida and California, where HMOs haven't paid the doctors' withhold or have suddenly pulled up and left town, or shut down. The three or four major players here seem to be honest, and physicians are satisfied with them.

*How do you persuade doctors to join a hospital organization like yours?*

If that person has been in practice before, I say, "Nothing changes. You do all the things you've always done. You have all the freedom you had before without the responsibilities. You can take vacations and not worry about losing your income. You have a guaranteed income, so you don't have to worry about being wiped out if you get sick. And your pay can increase as the hospital makes more money."

I tell other doctors that I no longer worry about the things I hated doing most in private practice. Billing, for example. I hated to confront patients about paying their bills. It didn't happen often, but I hated it. I hated to order supplies—that used to drive me nuts. I didn't like to be the person who made the decision about what I would charge for a service; I would much rather let an organization do it. Those are all advantages for a practicing physician.

You are of course working with hospital executives, who often don't understand medicine. Some of the things I consider important, they don't. If I need a battery or any small office item, for example, I just go out and buy it. That's a lot easier than calling the hospital and waiting for them to send one over. So then the executives say, "We've got those in our storeroom, why would you do that?"

*What would you tell doctors who have never had a private practice?*

For them, it's a little different. If they joined a managed-care organization right out of residency, they have never experienced the freedom that a practicing physician has. To them I say, "If you are interested in being an independent provider and having all the freedoms that a private practitioner in a small community would have, with little of the downside and with no outlay of money, this is the way to go. You don't have other physicians forcing you to do something you don't want to do; you don't have to fit into a mold the way you may have to in an HMO. An HMO can tell you how much you'll charge and when, how many patients you'll see, and what hours you'll work. With a hospital, those things are all negotiable. I don't see any downsides to this sort of relationship."

*How does the pay compare with private practice?*

Because of my experience, I make pretty good money—over $120,000. Somebody coming out of a residency would make less. But some hospitals are willing to pay as much as $150,000. I had one offer me that, with almost the same kind of arrangement I have here with St. John's.

Another hospital told me that if I would open a practice in a small community, it would pay me significantly more than I was making at St. John's; it needed not only my patients but the public relations boost of helping out the community with its doctor shortage. Public relations is important to hospitals now.

Of course, if your primary aim were making money, you could do what some doctors have done for years—selective billing. If you've got two procedure codes and one procedure costs more than the other, you bill for the more expensive one even though it's not quite what you did. But I don't do nor want to do those things.

*How many patients do you see on an average day?*

About 30, and that's too many. I know doctors who see between 50 and 60 a day. Can you believe that? They're trying to compete with the proceduralists and want to make $250,000. In private practice you have to see as many patients as possible to compete. But I can see 30 patients a day and keep my normal hospital load of about three patients, manage this office, and make $120,000. I don't make more because I'd have to see more patients. It takes me 15 minutes to get my mind going with each patient. I've got to shut off the last one and start thinking about the new one, get into his or her problems. That's not something I can do every five minutes. If we have an emergency and I get a bunch of patients dumped on me, more than I usually handle, I'm a mess

*How difficult has it been for you to come back to private practice after being in management for almost six years?*

Not hard at all. Of course, it's taken some adjustment. I found out, for example, that the drug companies have come out with a lot more blood pressure pills. There were seven or eight kinds when I left practice. Six years later there are 20, all brand-new. That took a little getting used to, even though I'd kept up with the medical literature.

But when I got back into practice, I felt a lot more comfortable. Most of my old patients came back right away. I just started up where I'd left off. I don't get bored with the patients or my practice—it helps that I'm a family practitioner. With some of the specialties, of course, you don't get that immediate gratification. Nobody thanks you for putting things up them like an X-ray tube or a colonoscope.

*You seem to get a kick out of medicine.*

Yes, I'm still having fun. Part of that is the people I deal with. Middletown, though not completely rural—the whole area between Muncie and Anderson has about 150,000 people—is small enough for the concerns of its residents and doctors to be radically different from those of large urban centers. Patients here have altogether different expectations of their doctors. They don't expect miracles. They don't expect medicine to be the answer to all their ills. When I have to tell a patient he's got cancer, he's likely to put his arm around me and say, "I'm sorry. I know it's hard on you to have to say that." They respond to the doctor as they would to a normal human being. And I relate to them the same way.

# CHAPTER five

# THE LURE OF INDEPENDENCE

For 17 years neurosurgeon Andrew Smith, the chairman and president-elect of the Minnesota Medical Association, had a thriving independent practice in Minneapolis. He worked on the staff of several hospitals, and his career as a neurosurgeon was successful and secure. Then, in 1994, Smith lost nearly half of his patients when a hospital he worked for merged with a large multispecialty clinic.

Smith, 51, realized that the same thing was happening to many independent practitioners. Those who had agreed to affiliate with a managed-care organization were going to thrive; those who had not were being squeezed out of the system. HMOs, PPOs, and other third-party payers had stopped expanding physician panels. For doctors who were not prepared to sign exclusive contracts, the options appeared frighteningly limited.

The crisis forced Smith to investigate how unaffiliated doctors in Minneapolis-St. Paul could compete in a market already dense with managed care. He and a few colleagues worked out a plan for an integrated physician network, a 750-doctor group practice operating from multiple sites, or clinic without walls. They wanted to offer physicians the benefits of a large group practice that wouldn't unduly infringe on their independence.

If his plan succeeds it will bring Smith a step closer to what he

*Dr. Andrew J. K. Smith*
*Neurosurgeon*

considers his greatest goal: "Convincing independent physicians that there is an alternative to selling their practices or becoming employed by a hospital or health plan."

*When you began your career, how did you envision your future?*
DR. SMITH: When I graduated from medical school, I thought physicians were in control of their destinies and that if they were willing to work hard and practice good medicine, they would be assured a steady stream of patients. Since I was willing to do both, I felt my future was secure.

*How has the introduction of managed care affected you?*

The threat of losing my independence has not affected me much emotionally. It has simply heightened my resolve to preserve what has always been good about independent practice—a close one-to-one relationship with patients, the right to choose the doctors I refer to, and a convenient location near my patients.

Managed care has also made me aware of the need to make surgical decisions that consider risk, benefit, *and* cost. I have to take the needs of the community into account along with the needs of my patient. Doctors have always cared for patients and their extended families. The concern for the community just carries the extended-family concept a bit further. This has in no way prevented me from being the doctor I want to be.

*Describe the medical environment in the Twin Cities.*

It's a place of rapidly diminishing options for independent doctors. My own story is a good example. As a neurosurgeon, I may on any given day operate at two or three places, principally at Methodist, a local community hospital with a medical staff of 800 or so. Half of Methodist's physicians are employed by Park Nicollet Medical Center, a large multispecialty, fully integrated group practice; the other half are independent practitioners. A few months ago, Methodist Hospital and Park Nicollet decided to integrate into one large corporation. What that did, of course, was leave the unaffiliated doctors on the medical staff very concerned about who was going to look after their interests. Would they continue to practice at the hospital? At about the same time, Park Nicollet decided they didn't need to contract with me; they could hire their own neurosurgeon. Overnight, half of my practice vanished.

The outlook for me as an independent practitioner in this kind of marketplace got sort of gloomy. So I started looking around. I had a good vantage point because of my position with the Minnesota Medical Association. I was very involved in medical policy development for the doctors' group.

*Did you consider joining a managed-care organization?*

Only very briefly. I feel too strongly about my independence—

as many doctors do—to sign exclusive contracts. I want to be in control of my destiny: I want to select my patients, I want control over my hours. If I work twice as hard, I want that to be reflected in my income. But it's really less a reimbursement thing than a "Who's in control?" sort of thing. I am in independent practice because I like to be a decision-maker. I don't want a large central administration to make decisions for me.

I began looking around and seeing that the way our community has been consolidating into fewer, larger health plans, it doesn't make any difference what kind of quality I provide or how hard I'm willing to work or even how little I'm willing to be paid. If somebody decides that they would rather employ another neurosurgeon, I simply may not be able to find work.

I quickly learned that I wasn't alone. Many individual practitioners were getting squeezed out of the market. A lot of them were deeply and justifiably worried about survival. They had noticed, as I had, that managed-care providers were locking up their physician panels and excluding those unwilling to throw their lot in exclusively with them. Many of us found ourselves in an impossible situation. We could keep our independence, but only at the cost of seeing our patient numbers fall by 50 percent, or more. Our practices couldn't survive.

*Why were the managed-care organizations locking up their panels?*

To remain profitable in a capitated environment, organizations like Blue Cross and Blue Shield, staff-model HMOs like Group Health, PPOs, and PHOs all have had to downsize their provider networks. They've had to focus on a smaller group of individuals with proven track records in cost-effectiveness and high-quality care. And if you hesitated about joining, you were left out of the game.

*How have you overcome the impasse?*

I began to see a glimmer of hope one day while my wife and I were sitting around in the basement just talking about the situation. We sat down at the word processor and wrote up a short analysis, just a couple of pages on the effects of consolidation on the local health care marketplace. What concerned me was not the question of managed care; it was access to patients. The central question I discussed with my wife was, Is there some structure that can allow those like me the measure of independence we need while still allowing us to thrive?

What I came up with was the idea of creating a metropolitan-wide, well-financed, professionally managed, doctor-owned alternative to the vertically integrated systems that dominate the local landscape—in essence, an organization that would provide capitation, accountability, risk-sharing, and anything else required by our marketplace.

*How did you get from analysis to execution?*

It wouldn't have been possible without the response I got from other physicians. When I presented my paper to medical societies around the state, I was astonished by the reaction. There were a lot of doctors in the same situation who were worried about their survival. A group of about 30 from the Minnesota Medical Association and two county medical societies got together to flesh out the idea.

Our first step was to meet with as diverse a group of physicians as we could to make sure that whatever we came up with would have broad appeal. Not an easy task, given that these are professionals who, often for very good reasons, chose to be independent. They don't necessarily agree on anything.

We then met with professional and legal consultants to spell out our concept of a clinic without walls. Once that was nailed down, the medical societies stepped back and a group of area doctors formed an interim board of 12 directors. We incorporated, chose a name—Criterion Health Care Network—defined the bylaws, decided to sell each member physician one share of stock as a way of financing the company, and selected the telecommunications network that would link the offices of the practitioners to each other and to the central business corporation. We established committees for credentialing, traveled around the Twin Cities area to explain the organization, started a newsletter, and did anything else we could to speed up the launch.

*How did the medical community respond, especially the independent doctors?*

Applications started to come in at a furious pace. The total number of independents isn't high, but the percentage of those who applied is mind-boggling. About 80 percent of the health care in the state is provided through managed-care vehicles. In the Minneapolis-St. Paul area, half the doctors are employed by large multispecialty clinics. That leaves approximately 2,000 unaffiliated doctors who might be interested in an organization like ours. As of today, 750 have applied—an incredible number. Simple math shows you how high a percentage that is. And the figure shows how desperate doctors are for credible alternatives to large managed-care organizations that leave individual practitioners with little control over their destinies. I can't go anywhere in town without people congratulating me or the group because we've come up with a reasonable alternative to the things doctors feared—losing patients, having to join a multispecialty clinic, or becoming an employee of a hospital or some kind of entity.

*How will Criterion be structured?*

It will revolve around a central business corporation that has provider contracts with each of the shareholders. The corporation will manage the system and oversee the network and integration; provider clinics will do the medical work. In many ways, this clinic without walls will operate like PPOs or IPAs, which have a central administration that contracts with providers. The difference with Criterion is that the doctors own the central corporation. We're creating a quasi-multispecialty clinic and managed-care company at the same time, all owned by physician shareholders.

*How will you find the most qualified doctors?*

As a new company, Criterion has the luxury of selecting physicians with proven track records in high-quality, cost-effective medicine. And we've got access to that data from a large indemnity insurance carrier and one of the largest regional HMOs. We're also looking at how many specialists of a certain type we need in each of the subregions within the Twin Cities area.

Our philosophy is to attract as many primary-care practitioners as we can, then get them to draw up a list of specialists and sub-specialists to whom they normally refer. That has given us a rich source of good doctors, especially combined with the data from the managed-care and indemnity insurance companies about the doctors' quality of care and cost-effectiveness. We have had so many people who want to join that we've been able to pick pretty much whomever we want.

*How do you plan to market Criterion?*

Some large buying coalitions, including representatives from Fortune 500 and Fortune 100 companies, have formed the Business Healthcare Action Group, a purchasing pool interested in integrated health care systems accountable for quality and outcome. We want an opportunity to network with them and any other Twin Cities purchasing pool. These pools seem to be the direction of health care in Minneapolis and St. Paul.

*What will Criterion offer the buyers?*

We'll offer capitated contracts because that is what our purchasers are accustomed to. But we will also offer services few other organizations do, such as outpatient electronic medical records accessible to all clinic members. That link is as important to the doctors as to our potential partners. One purchaser, Northwestern National Life, has been especially intrigued by the possibility of maintaining the independence of these practices. Doctors who affiliate with Criterion will run or own their own clinics, hire and fire their employees, and have their own pension and profit-sharing plans. But these doctors are linked for recruiting, billing, scheduling, and generating an outpatient electronic medical record; that means we've built automatic efficiencies into the system that are very attractive to area companies.

*How have you gotten started?*

Our first task has been to put together the physician network and to get contracts for patient care by negotiating with established

HMOs and indemnity companies. They would use our provider network; we would use their existing contracts.

We decided that an ideal network would be 500 to 800 physicians, with about 50 percent in primary care. That's in line with what experts are calling for nationally.

*What are your chances of success?*

We're optimistic. If we sell this concept of a partially integrated network to companies whose employees already see those same doctors, and if, as our research suggests, people prefer care from the doctors they've gone to for years over care delivered within one huge edifice housing 400 doctors—if we're successful in building on that marketing concept, then more and more patients will come to Criterion and back out to the providers through the networks.

In a region like the Twin Cities, where health care is market- and purchaser-driven and where purchasers are demanding the sort of entity we're creating with Criterion, an option like the one we're proposing is very attractive.

*How can Criterion be successful without dealing directly with hospitals?*

Hospitals will be part of the equation. Minnesota has become the only state in the country to legislate managed competition, and by July 1997 we will have to either be practicing as a so-called integrated service network (ISN) or as a modified, discounted fee-for-service system called the regulated all-payer option (RAPO). The RAPO system has fee controls and reporting requirements so onerous that state regulators are hoping everyone chooses the ISN model. An ISN is not just a group of doctors, but a group of doctors, hospitals, and nonphysician providers. That's very much in the back of our minds, and as we put the finishing touches on this clinic without walls, we want to form an integrated network large and powerful enough that it can, either through direct negotiation with the area hospitals or through managed-care companies, form an integrated service network. We're structurally prepared for it.

*Will doctors still be able to contract with PPOs and HMOs?*

Member physicians can contract with any other payers they wish.

In some instances, Criterion could start out being a small percentage of a doctor's practice. That will change as we become more successful in the marketplace and contract with strategic marketing partners. But nothing would preclude them from doing business outside of Criterion. We're not employing these doctors. We're giving them the option of owning a controlling interest in developing new sources of business.

*How much is the initial investment for each doctor?*

Seven hundred and fifty dollars. That will buy each doctor one share and one vote. The figure is low but it seems to be working well in our marketplace.

You'd be amazed at how doctors can squabble about it. It's not uncommon to hear, "Well, I put in $500 last year to join one company, and $1,000 for another." Many companies have asked providers to make a financial contribution if they want to become part of a network. For doctors in midsized groups the outlay of capital is substantial; some are becoming resistant to paying more. We thought it better to establish the network, invite doctors in at an obviously low dollar figure, and try to build value from there.

*Did other clinics without walls serve as models?*

Yes, including the Sacramento-Sierra Medical Group. But each state is different, with its own needs. In the competitive, highly integrated market of the Twin Cities, we needed something much bigger and bolder than any existing clinic without walls. We also had to be able to take risk and to work within a capitated environment, which is an even more constrained reimbursement environment than discounted fee for service. We could end up with disaster if we're undercapitalized in a large system like this and still have to provide care for the full term of the contract. So a look at existing models showed us that we needed to come up with a new animal altogether.

*What were the concerns of doctors interested in your organization?*

They asked questions like, Can the clinic integrate sufficiently to deal with capitation and prevent a cost hemorrhage that could bankrupt us? A lot of primary-care practitioners have been gatekeepers and have been doing reasonably well under capitated contracts for years. They wanted an organization knit tightly enough to control the different specialists and subspecialists. Primary-care gatekeepers in the Twin Cities have been capitated, but not the specialists and subspecialists. That has resulted in a we-versus-them mentality that can hurt the patient. Primary-care doctors might be loath to refer a patient even in circumstances that may call for it, because if they do, they could lose money. In Criterion, where both the primary-care doctors and the specialists are in the same risk pool, it is in everyone's interest to preserve quality while working together to save money.

*What is the high point of your medical career?*

My election as chairman of the Minnesota Medical Association was probably the most important moment in my professional life. I became someone others look to for long-term direction. I became a decision-maker.

# CHAPTER six

# DIRECTING
# CHANGE

D r. Brian Ely had been in private practice in Sacramento for several years when, in the early 1980s, he realized that managed care was eclipsing the conventional practice of medicine in California. Curious about where he might fit within the new system, he began talking to some family practitioners in a small HMO. "I felt that physicians should take the initiative and begin to organize [for managed care]," said Ely. At that time he heard about internists who were forming the Sacramento-Sierra Medical Group, then a 24-doctor clinic without walls. Creating a corporation with other physicians and yet maintaining his independence appealed to Ely, and in 1986 he joined the group. Four years later he became Sacramento-Sierra's medical director. The family practitioner who once found consolation in philosophy now found his satisfactions in reshaping his organization for managed care. In 1992 the group affiliated with the Sutter Medical Foundation. The organization currently has 81 doctors.

"When we affiliated, we were losing lots of money," said Ely, 44. "It was chaos here, and the physicians were almost depressed." Ely also felt torn. He was committed to managing the group, but still felt an obligation to see patients. Ultimately he chose management. "I decided to try to restore order and renew physicians' enjoyment of their practices," he said. "I think I've made a difference."

*Dr. Brian E. Ely*
*Family Practitioner*

Ely is comfortable in his new role and looks forward to helping revive what he calls "the healing relationship between doctor and patient, a relationship seriously disrupted in the last few years."

*How did you become interested in managed care?*
DR. ELY: My interest began as intellectual curiosity. I had started my practice in the mid-1980s, at the tail end of what doctors call the golden age of medicine, when physicians could charge what they wanted and have patients bill their insurance companies. But I quickly learned that the relationship would be changing, that

physicians would have much less control. Some people were going to be in and some out, and some organizations would be more successful than others in acquiring patients. I thought, *Let's see if I can figure out what's likely to happen and how I can be a part of it.* I didn't know anything about managed care, but I was in a position to be more open-minded than doctors who had already practiced for years. The changes were new and exciting, and I didn't have another way of looking at the world.

*How did you become involved with the Sacramento-Sierra group?*

In 1985 some internists contacted me who were developing a clinic without walls, then a new concept in managed care. It was hard to understand what they were doing except that they were forming a corporation with employees and benefits. I was interested but I waited about a year before joining so that I could gauge what else was going on in the community.

*Did other doctors accuse you of betraying the profession?*

Certainly not the people I worked with. And working for a clinic without walls by its nature made those issues moot.

*Were you asked to make a financial contribution?*

There was no buy-in, but there was a monthly charge to the individual practices for administration, so that you paid, say, $1,000 per month to support the corporate overhead. The fee was based on a sliding scale—specialists paid a little more than generalists. Nonmember specialists could make a monthly financial contribution to keep their option open to join.

*Why did you affiliate with Sutter?*

Because we learned that a clinic without walls is a transitional arrangement. It can't last forever. An organization can't succeed if individuals are just trying to do the best they can for themselves. To be permanent an organization has to be integrated and the doctors have to be working toward a common goal.

What we did as a clinic was take a bunch of individual practices and add a corporate superstructure to develop a larger patient base. But to be solvent we knew we would have to control the ancillary services like X-rays and labs. In the interim we had to support the

# Powerful Innovators

*Next to excellence is the appreciation of it.*

William Makepeace Thackeray

*Miles is pleased to sponsor this series on Powerful Innovators to remember, recognize, and appreciate the truly remarkable achievements of the best of the medical profession.*

*We salute these individuals; we applaud their efforts; we remember their deeds.*

*More importantly, we salute and applaud the efforts today's physicians make every day.*

H. Brian Allen, MD, FFPM
Director, Scientific Relations
Miles Inc.
Pharmaceutical Division

# Powerful Numbers

*speak for themselves:*

*2 ... The number of hours ciprofloxacin needed for complete killing* in vitro *of a representative isolate of* Pseudomonas aeruginosa, *a rate that was more than two times faster than that of ceftazidime, piperacillin, imipenem, or tobramycin.*\*

*4 ... The number of stages of cell growth during which ciprofloxacin actively kills— the lag, exponential growth, stationary, and dying-off phases.*\*

*96 ... The percent susceptibility of 71,389 clinical isolates of Enterobacteriaceae to ciprofloxacin.*\*

## The most potent fluoroquinolone.[1-3]\*

\**In vitro* activity does not necessarily imply a correlation with *in vivo* results.

*See complete prescribing information at the end of this book.*

© April 1992, Miles Inc. Pharmaceutical Division    Printed in U.S.A.    FO9202    MIL-6451

new administrative superstructure, and that meant we were losing money. Without a capital partner, we would just continue as a shoestring operation. Luckily, Sutter was interested in merging. It had the hospital and the facilities, but not the doctors.

*Who contacted whom?*

Sutter and the Sacramento-Sierra Medical Group had been talking about working together since Sacramento-Sierra's formation in 1984. Sutter hired and paid for our chief executive officer, and it has always provided some administrative financial support. I think that Sutter expected we would one day affiliate. It wanted to influence the direction of the changes in health care. And if it didn't protect its provider base, it wouldn't have any patients.

In theory, the administrative structure we now have creates an independent entity operating at the system level—separate from both the hospital and the doctor group. Sutter Medical Foundation owns our assets. The medical group doesn't own anything—not even a Q-tip. The foundation contracts our services and provides us with everything—facilities, support staff—and it does all the accounting functions, billing, everything.

*Is the group monitored by the foundation for efficiency or is there peer review of individual doctors?*

That's a good question. Only in the last year and a half have we begun to work on those issues with any energy. We began as a bunch of individual practices, and we've gone along with the offices doing their own thing. We did do credentialing, but we did nothing special in terms of quality control or performance. But compensation has precipitated a change. We decided that we needed a guaranteed income to hold on to our primary-care doctors. We knew that we also needed performance and quality standards. Last year we developed performance standards and decided on the number of office hours and patients each doctor should have. This year we're hiring someone to do a full-scale quality-assurance program, looking at everything from staffing to training.

*How would you persuade a doctor to join Sutter?*

I'd say that solo practice is no longer an option—at least in this area of the country. I'd explain that our intent at Sutter is to maximize physicians' independence and maintain the relationship between doctor and patient; that is, to make sure that every patient has his own doctor, that primary care is provided at a neighborhood level, and that doctors have some control over their schedules, working environment, and the people they work with, yet still have a support system that allows them to offer cost-effective care.

*How have the doctors responded to your plans for efficiency?*

No doctor is comfortable giving up control of patient care. They're used to being responsible for everything. We have to link pieces of the system so that doctors know that the things they are no longer doing are actually getting done. And we have to convince them that the system is safe and effective and cost-effective. We have to give them evidence, and the tools and the confidence to improve. We're not quite there yet.

In private practice physicians spend a lot of time answering phone calls and educating patients when others could do that. Registered nurses, for example, can handle phone questions and decide whether a patient needs to come in. They can take more time and respond in a more timely manner than a doctor. Physicians shouldn't have to struggle to get things done.

I want to take care of the most patients we can with the least resources, as long as we're doing a good job. I want care—I have trouble saying this precisely—provided at the lowest level of expertise necessary, so that midlevel practitioners do what they can do, registered nurses do what they can do, and so on. From a physician's perspective, that means doing what he or she finds most challenging and interesting.

*How much hand-holding do you do with the doctors in your group?*

A lot. Doctors need reassurance that things are going well. They can't always see where we're headed. They need to hear during this turbulent time where we're going, what we're doing, where we've gotten so far, and how it's working out.

*Do you have to reject many doctors who want to join Sutter?*

Not many primary-care practitioners. Some specialists have expressed interest in joining, but we want to be very careful about who and how many we pick. Sacramento has more than twice as many specialists as primary doctors. Primary-care doctors are the critical piece in the capitated-care equation, and they will always have plenty of work. But we don't have enough patients to meet the needs of specialists here, and as panels develop to provide care, some specialists are going to be left out—the ones who aren't ready to think about capitation. Those who want to be cooperative, who can work with primary-care groups and conceive of doing things differently are going to get the business; the others won't.

I'm interested in putting together a curriculum that would allow us to identify which specialties might most easily fill whatever gaps we have in primary care. We're probably going to start with a specialty like ob-gyn. We'd tell those doctors that to become part of our group as primary-care physicians, they would have to complete some courses in primary care that we would arrange for them.

*Would specialists have to accept lower pay?*

Well, primary care doesn't pay as well—or hasn't in the past. Given the current demand for primary-care physicians and the glut of specialists, primary-care income will probably be stable and specialty income will drop. For those specialists who aren't able to capture a big part of the market, it's going to drop like a rock.

*How would you describe your patient base?*

We still take fee-for-service patients. Medicare and capitated patients account for 70 to 75 percent of our practice. The 81 doctors in our group take care of approximately 100,000 patients—a third of those are capitated.

*Do you think that the basis of a doctor's income is changing?*

Absolutely. We're completely revising the economic system, even though one of the main benefits or attractions of medicine has been financial security. That's disappearing for many doctors, particularly specialists. For primary-care physicians, not so much, but they are going through other changes. Instead of the old fee-for-service arrangement, for example, we're getting into these system deals, which are very different conceptually; primary-care doctors are working for systems that offer salaries or capitation.

Many doctors don't understand where managed care is going. You can talk about it with them, but they lose focus quickly when they have to deal with angry patients who can't see the specialist they've always seen. These doctors can easily lapse into a reactive anger.

I just read a book about the Civil War that described some of the economic upheaval that the South experienced. An old order was turned out in a few years. We're going through something similar in health care. It's revolutionary.

*What do you think frightens doctors about capitation?*

Physicians still think of medicine as as a cottage industry. They're used to doing piecework: I do something, I get paid for it. The idea of getting paid indirectly to do all care—they just can't grasp that. And they're very emotional on this issue. Everyone has heard about a bad experience with capitation. It's hard to keep an open mind.

But salary and capitation are the future for doctors in managed care. Ideally a managed-care organization should decide what it will pay for professional services and allow you to break that down by specialties. If you have physicians on salary, then your budget combines their salaries and the cost of contract physicians. For outside services, you could decide a budget for, say, neurosurgery based on national standards, and then contract with some neurosurgeons. At Sutter, I think we'll see some services provided by a salaried group and others by outsiders on a capitated basis.

*You've mentioned independence a couple of times. How much autonomy do physicians affiliated with Sutter have?*

Doctors have to work a minimum number of hours and have a fixed amount of vacation, but within that structure they have a lot to say about when they come and go, when they take vacations, and who works in their offices. In general doctors are individualists who want control of their lives. That usually means they want control over their micro-environment. You can talk about governance issues and who orders the paper towels, but that's not what is most important to them. They want control over their employees. They want people working for them they like. They want a say about what the office looks like and what their patient load is.

*How does Sutter pay its physicians?*

We changed in 1994 to a salary system which still emphasizes productivity—it encourages people to work hard and rewards them for efficiency and quality.

*As the medical director, what do you look for in a physician interested in joining the foundation?*

For the most part, the qualities you want in any good physician, except that the doctor can't be married to a particular perspective on health care. Some physicians tend to develop opinions that may have worked at one time but don't anymore, and they lose track of the general principles. For example, there has been tremendous resistance to capitation. In fact, managed fee-for-service compensation has gotten as low here as anywhere in the country because doctors have accepted huge discounts to avoid capitation. It's almost bizarre; many doctors just haven't been able to grasp the idea of capitation or suspend disbelief to see if it will work.

No one's asking physicians to practice second-rate medicine, but they do need to reexamine their assumptions about what's necessary. They are doing a lot of things they don't need to do. And doing only what's necessary doesn't always mean doing the least expensive task; it may mean doing the more expensive procedure and getting the answer sooner.

*What qualities made you a good candidate for medical director?*

You have to be willing. You probably should have a background in primary care. And you have to have a system perspective. It's possible to be a good physician by focusing only on the individual patient. But to be a medical director, you need to understand the perspectives of insurance companies, hospitals, physician groups, and specialties, as well as government intentions and the general direction of health care. You have to anticipate change and have a clear idea of what you're working toward.

The position evolved gradually. I was the chairman of the medical group's utilization-review department, and as managed care became a bigger part of our practice and as the system grew, I developed a picture about where we needed to go. I also realized that I couldn't do an adequate job unless I focused more exclusively on the administrative part of what I did.

*Do you continue to see patients?*

I still practice a couple of days a week. Until you are willing to let go of primary responsibility for the care of your patients, they have to come first. People don't die if you miss a meeting or a project deadline.

Giving up patient care has been problematic. I don't have the opportunity to provide continuing care because I'm not there consistently for my patients. But I need to keep up with the practice enough to know what's going on and to maintain some practice skills. What I may do is move toward urgent care in the next few months—just see acute problems. I've resisted that because I didn't want to let go of the people I've been taking care of for so long, but to keep seeing regular patients is not practical. My patients are not happy, and I'm not happy.

*Was it a hard decision to move into management?*

Just making the choice was the hardest thing—I was always torn about whether it was a good thing to do. My dad was a doctor, and what I remember about his practice was how much he talked on the phone to patients. He really enjoyed his practice. So I always thought of primary care as real medicine, and that's what I wanted to do. The attraction for me was the doctor-patient relationship.

When I finally decided to choose management, I knew that in the long run I'd have more impact. It wasn't an easy choice, because once you stop practicing regularly you start to lose touch with your clinical skills. And that's scary. But I do feel that I'm giving the job the attention it needs and that I'm doing a good job.

One advantage of management is that when I'm off work, I'm off work. I don't get calls in the middle of the night, and I don't have to rush. I don't have to leave meetings to go take care of a patient. The unexpected is no longer a part of my job. On the other hand, some of the stress is worse because if I fail, my failure affects 81 doctors. I take that personally.

*What's your perspective on managed care now that you've been involved for almost a decade?*

Since I started practice, I've seen some of my worst fears realized. Large numbers of patients have had to shift from one doctor to another because of contract changes. We've seen the rise of third parties, utilization-review people overseeing care and adjudicating requests for services. We've seen divisions within the medical community as patients have had to choose between their family practitioner and their ob-gyn, or between one specialist and another, simply because the doctors belong to different panels now.

I've tried to make things better at Sutter. I'm doing everything I can, for example, to have primary-care physicians—whom patients identify as their personal physicians—operate without worry about financial and contractual constraints. To do that, you need a panel of doctors who have a history of working well together so that the patient isn't affected by disgruntled physicians complaining about the plan. We've put together a more or less unified group in which doctors cooperate and respect each other. And the economic arrangements reward behavior that is constructive and efficient.

*Collegiality seems to be an important quality for you.*

I don't want doctors to be inefficient, but I'm most concerned about quality and being a team player. We want good, confident physicians who are respected in their communities and who have demonstrated an ability to work in a group environment. There are excellent physicians who have a great bedside manner and are beloved of their patients and work very hard who nevertheless cannot function in a group.

*What do you expect to be doing five years from now?*

I've taken some business and management courses here and there, and I'm going to start an M.B.A. program this fall. I like problem-solving and taking what I have and putting it together to make systems work. My greatest fear is that everything will get fixed and I won't have anything to do. I liked taking care of patients, but it wasn't enough of a challenge. The chaos in medical economics right now is a tremendous challenge.

# Additional Copies

To order copies of *The New Physician* for friends or colleagues,
please write to The Grand Rounds Press, Whittle Books,
333 Main St., Knoxville, Tenn. 37902. Please include the recipient's name,
mailing address, and, where applicable, primary specialty and ME number.

For a single copy, please enclose a check for $21.95 plus $3.50 for postage and
handling, payable to The Grand Rounds Press. Quantities may be limited.
Discounts apply to bulk orders when available. To order by phone using your
MasterCard or Visa card, please call 800-765-5889.

Also available, at the same price, are copies of the previous books from
The Grand Rounds Press:

*The Doctor Watchers* by Spencer Vibbert
*The New Genetics* by Leon Jaroff
*Surgeon Koop* by Gregg Easterbrook
*Inside Medical Washington* by James H. Sammons, M.D.
*Medicine For Sale* by Richard Currey
*The Doctor Dilemma* by Gerald R. Weissmann, M.D.
*Taking Care of Your Own* by Perri Klass, M.D.
*The Logic of Health-Care Reform* by Paul Starr
*Raising the Dead* by Richard Selzer
*Malpractice Solutions* by James Rosenblum
*What Works* by Spencer Vibbert

MD/2000:
*Revolution* by Russell C. Coile Jr.
*Decision Point* by Michael B. Guthrie, M.D.
*On Your Terms* by Steven Gittelson

Please allow four weeks for delivery.
Tennessee residents must add 8$1/4$ percent sales tax.

PRESCRIBING INFORMATION
APPENDIX

# CIPRO® I.V.
## (ciprofloxacin)
## For Intravenous Infusion

PZ100736

## DESCRIPTION

Cipro® I.V. (ciprofloxacin) is a synthetic broad-spectrum antimicrobial agent for intravenous (iv) administration. Ciprofloxacin, a fluoroquinolone, is 1-cyclopropyl-6-fluoro-1, 4-dihydro-4-oxo-7-(1-piperazinyl)-3-quinolinecarboxylic acid. Its empirical formula is $C_{17}H_{18}FN_3O_3$ and its chemical structure is:

Ciprofloxacin is a faint to light yellow crystalline powder with a molecular weight of 331.4. It is soluble in dilute (0.1N) hydrochloric acid and is practically insoluble in water and ethanol. Ciprofloxacin differs from other quinolones in that it has a fluorine atom at the 6-position, a piperazine moiety at the 7-position, and a cyclopropyl ring at the 1-position. Cipro® I.V. solutions are available as 1.0% aqueous concentrates, which are intended for dilution prior to administration, and as a 0.2% ready-for-use infusion solution in 5% Dextrose Injection. All formulas contain lactic acid as a solubilizing agent and hydrochloric acid for pH adjustment. The pH range for the 1.0% aqueous concentrates in vials is 3.3 to 3.9. The pH range for the 0.2% ready-for-use infusion solutions is 3.5 to 4.6.

The plastic container is fabricated from a specially formulated polyvinyl chloride. Solutions in contact with the plastic container can leach out certain of its chemical components in very small amounts within the expiration period, e.g., di(2-ethylhexyl) phthalate (DEHP), up to 5 parts per million. The suitability of the plastic has been confirmed in tests in animals according to USP biological tests for plastic containers as well as by tissue culture toxicity studies.

## CLINICAL PHARMACOLOGY

Following 60-minute intravenous infusions of 200 mg and 400 mg ciprofloxacin to normal volunteers, the mean maximum serum concentrations achieved were 2.1 and 4.6 µg/mL, respectively; the concentrations at 12 hours were 0.1 and 0.2 µg/mL, respectively.

### Steady-state Ciprofloxacin Serum Concentrations (µg/mL) After 60-minute IV Infusions q 12 h.

| Dose | 30 min. | 1 hr | 3 hr | 6 hr | 8 hr | 12 hr |
|---|---|---|---|---|---|---|
| 200 mg | 1.7 | 2.1 | 0.6 | 0.3 | 0.2 | 0.1 |
| 400 mg | 3.7 | 4.6 | 1.3 | 0.7 | 0.5 | 0.2 |

The pharmacokinetics of ciprofloxacin are linear over the dose range of 200 to 400 mg administered intravenously. The serum elimination half-life is approximately 5–6 hours and the total clearance is around 35 L/hr. Comparison of the pharmacokinetic parameters following the 1st and 5th iv dose on a q 12 h regimen indicates no evidence of drug accumulation.

The absolute bioavailability of oral ciprofloxacin is within a range of 70–80% with no substantial loss by first pass metabolism. An intravenous infusion of 400 mg ciprofloxacin given over 60 minutes every 12 hours has been shown to produce an area under the serum concentration time curve (AUC) equivalent to that produced by a 500 mg oral dose given every 12 hours. A 400 mg iv dose administered over 60 minutes every 12 hours results in a $C_{max}$ similar to that observed with a 750 mg oral dose. An infusion of 200 mg ciprofloxacin given every 12 hours produces an AUC equivalent to that produced by a 250 mg oral dose given every 12 hours.

After intravenous administration, approximately 50% to 70% of the dose is excreted in the urine as unchanged drug. Following a 200 mg iv dose, concentrations in the urine usually exceed 200 µg/mL 0–2 hours after dosing and are generally greater than 15 µg/mL 8–12 hours after dosing. Following a 400 mg iv dose, urine concentrations generally exceed 400 µg/mL 0–2 hours after dosing and are usually greater than 30 µg/mL 8–12 hours after dosing. The renal clearance is approximately 22 L/hr. The urinary excretion of ciprofloxacin is virtually complete by 24 hours after dosing.

Co-administration of probenecid with ciprofloxacin results in about a 50% reduction in the ciprofloxacin renal clearance and a 50% increase in its concentration in the systemic circulation. Although bile concentrations of ciprofloxacin are severalfold higher than serum concentrations after intravenous dosing, only a small amount of the administered dose (<1%) is recovered from the bile as unchanged drug. Approximately 15% of an iv dose is recovered from the feces within 5 days after dosing.

After iv administration, three metabolites of ciprofloxacin have been identified in human urine which together account for approximately 10% of the intravenous dose.

In patients with reduced renal function, the half-life of ciprofloxacin is slightly prolonged and dosage adjustments may be required. (See DOSAGE AND ADMINISTRATION.)

In preliminary studies in patients with stable chronic liver cirrhosis, no significant changes in ciprofloxacin pharmacokinetics have been observed. However, the kinetics of ciprofloxacin in patients with acute hepatic insufficiency have not been fully elucidated.

The binding of ciprofloxacin to serum proteins is 20 to 40%.

After intravenous administration, ciprofloxacin is present in saliva, nasal and bronchial secretions, sputum, skin blister fluid, lymph, peritoneal fluid, bile and prostatic secretions. It has also been detected in the lung, skin, fat, muscle, cartilage and bone. Although the drug diffuses into cerebrospinal fluid (CSF), CSF concentrations are generally less than 10% of peak serum concentrations. Levels of the drug in the aqueous and vitreous chambers of the eye are lower than in serum.

**Microbiology:** Ciprofloxacin has *in vitro* activity against a wide range of gramnegative and gram-positive organisms. The bactericidal action of ciprofloxacin results from interference with the enzyme DNA gyrase which is needed for the synthesis of bacterial DNA.

Ciprofloxacin has been shown to be active against most strains of the following organisms both *in vitro* and in clinical infections. (See INDICATIONS AND USAGE section.)

### Gram-positive bacteria
*Enterococcus faecalis* (Many strains are only moderately susceptible)
*Staphylococcus aureus*
*Staphylococcus epidermidis*
*Streptococcus pneumoniae*
*Streptococcus pyogenes*

### Gram-negative bacteria
| | |
|---|---|
| *Citrobacter diversus* | *Morganella morganii* |
| *Citrobacter freundii* | *Proteus mirabilis* |
| *Enterobacter cloacae* | *Proteus vulgaris* |
| *Escherichia coli* | *Providencia rettgeri* |
| *Haemophilus influenzae* | *Providencia stuartii* |
| *Haemophilus parainfluenzae* | *Pseudomonas aeruginosa* |
| *Klebsiella pneumoniae* | *Serratia marcescens* |

Ciprofloxacin has been shown to be active *in vitro* against most strains of the following organisms; however, *the clinical significance of these data is unknown.*

### Gram-positive bacteria
*Staphylococcus haemolyticus*
*Staphylococcus hominis*
*Staphylococcus saprophyticus*

### Gram-negative bacteria
| | |
|---|---|
| *Acinetobacter calcoaceticus* | *Neisseria gonorrhoeae* |
| *Aeromonas caviae* | *Neisseria meningitidis* |
| *Aeromonas hydrophila* | *Pasteurella multocida* |
| *Brucella melitensis* | *Salmonella enteritidis* |
| *Campylobacter coli* | *Salmonella typhi* |
| *Campylobacter jejuni* | *Shigella flexneri* |
| *Edwardsiella tarda* | *Shigella sonnei* |
| *Enterobacter aerogenes* | *Vibrio cholerae* |
| *Haemophilus ducreyi* | *Vibrio parahaemolyticus* |
| *Klebsiella oxytoca* | *Vibrio vulnificus* |
| *Legionella pneumophila* | *Yersinia enterocolitica* |
| *Moraxella (Branhamella) catarrhalis* | |

### Other organisms
*Chlamydia trachomatis* (only moderately susceptible)
*Mycobacterium tuberculosis* (only moderately susceptible)

Most strains of *Pseudomonas cepacia* and some strains of *Pseudomonas maltophilia* are resistant to ciprofloxacin as are most anaerobic bacteria, including *Bacteroides fragilis* and *Clostridium difficile.*

Ciprofloxacin is slightly less active when tested at acidic pH. The inoculum size has little effect when tested *in vitro.* The minimum bactericidal concentration (MBC) generally does not exceed the minimum inhibitory concentration (MIC) by more than a factor of 2. Resistance to ciprofloxacin *in vitro* usually develops slowly (multiple-step mutation).

Ciprofloxacin does not cross-react with other antimicrobial agents such as betalactams or aminoglycosides; therefore, organisms resistant to these drugs may be susceptible to ciprofloxacin.

*In vitro* studies have shown that additive activity often results when ciprofloxacin is combined with other antimicrobial agents such as beta-lactams, aminoglycosides, clindamycin, or metronidazole. Synergy has been reported particularly with the combination of ciprofloxacin and a beta-lactam; antagonism is observed only rarely.

### Susceptibility Tests

**Diffusion Techniques:** Quantitative methods that require measurement of zone diameters give the most precise estimates of antibiotic susceptibility. One such procedure recommended for use with the 5-µg ciprofloxacin disk is the National Committee for Clinical Laboratory Standards (NCCLS) approved procedure (M2-A4--Performance Standards for Antimicrobial Disc Susceptibility Tests 1990). Only a 5-µg ciprofloxacin disk should be used, and it should not be used for testing susceptibility to less active quinolones; there are no suitable surrogate disks.

Results of laboratory tests using 5-µg ciprofloxacin disks should be interpreted using the following criteria:

| Zone Diameter (mm) | Interpretation |
|---|---|
| ≥ 21 | (S) Susceptible |
| 16 - 20 | (MS) Moderately Susceptible |
| ≤ 15 | (R) Resistant |

**Dilution Techniques:** Broth and agar dilution methods, such as those recommended by the NCCLS (M7-A2--Methods for Dilution Antimicrobial Susceptibility Tests for Bacteria that Grow Aerobically 1990), may be used to determine the minimum inhibitory concentration (MIC) of ciprofloxacin. MIC test results should be interpreted according to the following criteria:

| MIC (µg/mL) | Interpretation |
|---|---|
| ≤ 1 | (S) Susceptible |
| 2 | (MS) Moderately Susceptible |
| ≥ 4 | (R) Resistant |

For any susceptibility test, a report of "susceptible" indicates that the pathogen is likely to be inhibited by generally achievable blood levels. A report of "resistant" indicates that the pathogen is not likely to respond. A report of "moderately susceptible" indicates that the pathogen is expected to be susceptible to ciprofloxacin if high doses are used, or if the infection is confined to tissues and fluids in which high ciprofloxacin levels are attained.

The Quality Control (QC) strains should have the following assigned daily ranges for ciprofloxacin.

| QC Strains | Disk Zone Diameter (mm) | MIC (µg/mL) |
|---|---|---|
| *S. aureus* (ATCC 25923) | 22 – 30 | —— |
| *S. aureus* (ATCC 29213) | —— | 0.12 – 0.5 |
| *E. coli* (ATCC 25922) | 30 – 40 | 0.004 – 0.015 |
| *P. aeruginosa* (ATCC 27853) | 25 – 33 | 0.25 – 1.0 |
| *E. faecalis* (ATCC 29212) | —— | 0.25 – 2.0 |

## INDICATIONS AND USAGE

Cipro® I.V. is indicated for the treatment of infections caused by susceptible strains of the designated microorganisms in the conditions listed below when the intravenous administration offers a route of administration advantageous to the patient:

**Urinary Tract Infections – mild, moderate, severe and complicated infections** caused by *Escherichia coli*, (including cases with secondary bacteremia), *Klebsiella pneumoniae* subspecies *pneumoniae*, *Enterobacter cloacae*, *Serratia marcescens*, *Proteus mirabilis*, *Providencia rettgeri*, *Morganella morganii*, *Citrobacter diversus*, *Citrobacter freundii*, *Pseudomonas aeruginosa*, *Staphylococcus epidermidis*, and *Enterococcus faecalis*.

Cipro® I.V. is also indicated for the treatment of mild to moderate lower respiratory tract infections, skin and skin structure infections and bone and joint infections due to the organisms listed in each section below. In severe and complicated lower respiratory tract infections, skin and skin structure infections and bone and joint infections, safety and effectiveness of the iv formulation have not been established.

**Lower Respiratory Infections – mild to moderate infections** caused by *Escherichia coli*, *Klebsiella pneumoniae* subspecies *pneumoniae*, *Enterobacter cloacae*, *Proteus mirabilis*, *Pseudomonas aeruginosa*, *Haemophilus influenzae*, *Haemophilus parainfluenzae*, and *Streptococcus pneumoniae*.

**Skin and Skin Structure Infections – mild to moderate infections** caused by *Escherichia coli*, *Klebsiella pneumoniae* subspecies *pneumoniae*, *Enterobacter cloacae*, *Proteus mirabilis*, *Proteus vulgaris*, *Providencia stuartii*, *Morganella morganii*, *Citrobacter freundii*, *Pseudomonas aeruginosa*, *Staphylococcus aureus*, *Staphylococcus epidermidis*, and *Streptococcus pyogenes*.

**Bone and Joint Infections – mild to moderate infections** caused by *Enterobacter cloacae*, *Serratia marcescens*, and *Pseudomonas aeruginosa*.

If anaerobic organisms are suspected of contributing to the infection, appropriate therapy should be administered.

Appropriate culture and susceptibility tests should be performed before treatment in order to isolate and identify organisms causing infection and to determine their susceptibility to ciprofloxacin. Therapy with Cipro® I.V. may be initiated before results of these tests are known; once results become available, appropriate therapy should be continued.

As with other drugs, some strains of *Pseudomonas aeruginosa* may develop resistance fairly rapidly during treatment with ciprofloxacin. Culture and susceptibility testing performed periodically during therapy will provide information not only on the therapeutic effect of the antimicrobial agent but also on the possible emergence of bacterial resistance.

## CONTRAINDICATIONS

Cipro® I.V. (ciprofloxacin) is contraindicated in persons with a history of hypersensitivity to ciprofloxacin or any member of the quinolone class of antimicrobial agents.

## WARNINGS

**THE SAFETY AND EFFECTIVENESS OF CIPROFLOXACIN IN CHILDREN, ADOLESCENTS (LESS THAN 18 YEARS OF AGE), PREGNANT WOMEN, AND LACTATING WOMEN HAVE NOT BEEN ESTABLISHED. (SEE PRECAUTIONS - PEDIATRIC USE, PREGNANCY AND NURSING MOTHERS SUBSECTIONS.)** Ciprofloxacin causes lameness in immature dogs. Histopathological examination of the weight-bearing joints of these dogs revealed permanent lesions of the cartilage. Related quinolone-class drugs also produce erosions of cartilage of weight-bearing joints and other signs of arthropathy in immature animals of various species. (See ANIMAL PHARMACOLOGY.)

Convulsions have been reported in patients receiving ciprofloxacin. Convulsions, increased intracranial pressure, and toxic psychosis have been reported in patients receiving ciprofloxacin and other drugs of this class. Quinolones may also cause central nervous system (CNS) stimulation which may lead to tremors, restlessness, lightheadedness, confusion and hallucinations. If these reactions occur in patients receiving ciprofloxacin, the drug should be discontinued and appropriate measures instituted. As with all quinolones, ciprofloxacin should be used with caution in patients with known or suspected CNS disorders, such as severe cerebral arteriosclerosis, epilepsy, and other factors that predispose to seizures. (See ADVERSE REACTIONS.)

**SERIOUS AND FATAL REACTIONS HAVE BEEN REPORTED IN PATIENTS RECEIVING CONCURRENT ADMINISTRATION OF INTRAVENOUS CIPROFLOXACIN AND THEOPHYLLINE.** These reactions have included cardiac arrest, seizure, status epilepticus and respiratory failure. Although similar serious adverse events have been reported in patients receiving theophylline alone, the possibility that these reactions may be potentiated by ciprofloxacin cannot be eliminated. If concomitant use cannot be avoided, serum levels of theophylline should be monitored and dosage adjustments made as appropriate.

Serious and occasionally fatal hypersensitivity (anaphylactic) reactions, some following the first dose, have been reported in patients receiving quinolone therapy. Some reactions were accompanied by cardiovascular collapse, loss of consciousness, tingling, pharyngeal or facial edema, dyspnea, urticaria, and itching. Only a few patients had a history of hypersensitivity reactions. Serious anaphylactic reactions require immediate emergency treatment with epinephrine and other resuscitation measures, including oxygen, intravenous fluids, intravenous antihistamines, corticosteroids, pressor amines and airway management, as clinically indicated.

Severe hypersensitivity reactions characterized by rash, fever, eosinophilia, jaundice, and hepatic necrosis with fatal outcome have also been reported extremely rarely in patients receiving ciprofloxacin along with other drugs. The possibility that these reactions were related to ciprofloxacin cannot be excluded. Ciprofloxacin should be discontinued at the first appearance of a skin rash or any other sign of hypersensitivity.

**Pseudomembranous colitis has been reported with nearly all antibacterial agents, including ciprofloxacin, and may range in severity from mild to life-threatening. Therefore, it is important to consider this diagnosis in patients who present with diarrhea subsequent to the administration of antibacterial agents.**

Treatment with antibacterial agents alters the normal flora of the colon and may permit overgrowth of clostridia. Studies indicate that a toxin produced by *Clostridium difficile* is one primary cause of "antibiotic-associated colitis".

After the diagnosis of pseudomembranous colitis has been established, therapeutic measures should be initiated. Mild cases of pseudomembranous colitis usually respond to drug discontinuation alone. In moderate to severe cases, consideration should be given to management with fluids and electrolytes, protein supplementation and treatment with an antibacterial drug effective against *C. difficile*.

## PRECAUTIONS

**General:** INTRAVENOUS CIPROFLOXACIN SHOULD BE ADMINISTERED BY SLOW INFUSION OVER A PERIOD OF 60 MINUTES. Local iv site reactions have been reported with the intravenous administration of ciprofloxacin. These reactions are more frequent if infusion time is 30 minutes or less or if small veins of the hand are used. (See ADVERSE REACTIONS.)

Crystals of ciprofloxacin have been observed rarely in the urine of human subjects but more frequently in the urine of laboratory animals, which is usually alkaline. (See ANIMAL PHARMACOLOGY.) Crystalluria related to ciprofloxacin has been reported only rarely in humans because human urine is usually acidic. Alkalinity of the urine should be avoided in patients receiving ciprofloxacin. Patients should be well hydrated to prevent the formation of highly concentrated urine.

Alteration of the dosage regimen is necessary for patients with impairment of renal function. (See DOSAGE AND ADMINISTRATION.)

Moderate to severe phototoxicity manifested by an exaggerated sunburn reaction has been observed in some patients who were exposed to direct sunlight while receiving some members of the quinolone class of drugs. Excessive sunlight should be avoided.

As with any potent drug, periodic assessment of organ system functions, including renal, hepatic, and hematopoietic, is advisable during prolonged therapy.

**Information for Patients:** Patients should be advised that ciprofloxacin may be associated with hypersensitivity reactions, even following a single dose, and to discontinue the drug at the first sign of a skin rash or other allergic reaction.

Ciprofloxacin may cause dizziness and lightheadedness; therefore, patients should know how they react to this drug before they operate an automobile or machinery or engage in activities requiring mental alertness or coordination.

Patients should be advised that ciprofloxacin may increase the effects of theophylline and caffeine. There is a possibility of caffeine accumulation when products containing caffeine are consumed while taking quinolones.

**Drug Interactions:** As with other quinolones, concurrent administration of ciprofloxacin with theophylline may lead to elevated serum concentrations of theophylline and prolongation of its elimination half-life. This may result in increased risk of theophylline-related adverse reactions. (See WARNINGS.) If concomitant use cannot be avoided, serum levels of theophylline should be monitored and dosage adjustments made as appropriate.

Some quinolones, including ciprofloxacin, have also been shown to interfere with the metabolism of caffeine. This may lead to reduced clearance of caffeine and a prolongation of its serum half-life.

Some quinolones, including ciprofloxacin, have been associated with transient elevations in serum creatinine in patients receiving cyclosporine concomitantly.

Quinolones have been reported to enhance the effects of the oral anticoagulant warfarin or its derivatives. When these products are administered concomitantly, prothrombin time or other suitable coagulation tests should be closely monitored.

Probenecid interferes with renal tubular secretion of ciprofloxacin and produces an increase in the level of ciprofloxacin in the serum. This should be considered if patients are receiving both drugs concomitantly.

As with other broad-spectrum antimicrobial agents, prolonged use of ciprofloxacin may result in overgrowth of nonsusceptible organisms. Repeated evaluation of the patient's condition and microbial susceptibility testing are essential. If superinfection occurs during therapy, appropriate measures should be taken.

**Carcinogenesis, Mutagenesis, Impairment of Fertility:** Eight *in vitro* mutagenicity tests have been conducted with ciprofloxacin. Test results are listed below:

*Salmonella*/Microsome Test (Negative)
*E. coli* DNA Repair Assay (Negative)
Mouse Lymphoma Cell Forward Mutation Assay (Positive)
Chinese Hamster $V_{79}$ Cell HGPRT Test (Negative)
Syrian Hamster Embryo Cell Transformation Assay (Negative)
*Saccharomyces cerevisiae* Point Mutation Assay (Negative)
*Saccharomyces cerevisiae* Mitotic Crossover and Gene Conversion
Assay (Negative)
Rat Hepatocyte DNA Repair Assay (Positive)

Thus, two of the eight tests were positive, but results of the following three *in vivo* test systems gave negative results:

Rat Hepatocyte DNA Repair Assay
Micronucleus Test (Mice)
Dominant Lethal Test (Mice)

Long-term carcinogenicity studies in mice and rats have been completed. After daily oral dosing for up to 2 years, there is no evidence that ciprofloxacin has any carcinogenic or tumorigenic effects in these species.

**Pregnancy: Teratogenic Effects. Pregnancy Category C:** Reproduction studies have been performed in rats and mice at doses up to 6 times the usual daily human dose and have revealed no evidence of impaired fertility or harm to the fetus due to ciprofloxacin. In rabbits, ciprofloxacin (30 and 100 mg/kg orally) produced gastrointestinal disturbances resulting in maternal weight loss and an increased incidence of abortion. No teratogenicity was observed at either dose. After intravenous administration of doses up to 20 mg/kg, no maternal toxicity was produced, and no embryotoxicity or teratogenicity was observed. There are, however, no adequate and well-controlled studies in pregnant women. Ciprofloxacin should be used during pregnancy only if the potential benefit justifies the potential risk to the fetus. (See WARNINGS.)

**Nursing Mothers:** Ciprofloxacin is excreted in human milk. Because of the potential for serious adverse reactions in infants nursing from mothers taking ciprofloxacin, a decision should be made either to discontinue nursing or to discontinue the drug, taking into account the importance of the drug to the mother.

**Pediatric Use:** Safety and effectiveness in children and adolescents less than 18 years of age have not been established. Ciprofloxacin causes arthropathy in juvenile animals. (See WARNINGS.)

## ADVERSE REACTIONS

The most frequently reported events, without regard to drug relationship, among patients treated with intravenous ciprofloxacin were nausea, diarrhea, central nervous system disturbance, local iv site reactions, abnormalities of liver associated enzymes (hepatic enzymes) and eosinophilia. Headache, restlessness and rash were also noted in greater than 1% of patients treated with the most common doses of ciprofloxacin.

Local iv site reactions have been reported with the intravenous administration of ciprofloxacin. These reactions are more frequent if the infusion time is 30 minutes or less. These may appear as local skin reactions which resolve rapidly upon completion of the infusion. Subsequent intravenous administration is not contraindicated unless the reactions recur or worsen.

Additional events, without regard to drug relationship or route of administration, that occurred in 1% or less of ciprofloxacin courses are listed below:

GASTROINTESTINAL: ileus; jaundice; gastrointestinal bleeding; *C. difficile* associated diarrhea; pseudomembranous colitis; pancreatitis; hepatic necrosis; intestinal perforation; dyspepsia; epigastric or abdominal pain; vomiting; constipation; oral ulceration; oral candidiasis; mouth dryness; anorexia; dysphagia; flatulence.

CENTRAL NERVOUS SYSTEM: convulsive seizures, paranoia, toxic psychosis, depression, dysphasia, phobia, depersonalization, manic reaction, unresponsiveness, ataxia, confusion, hallucinations, dizziness, lightheadedness, paresthesia, anxiety, tremor, insomnia, nightmares, weakness, drowsiness, irritability, malaise, lethargy.

SKIN/HYPERSENSITIVITY: anaphylactic reactions; erythema multiforme/-Stevens-Johnson syndrome; exfoliative dermatitis; toxic epidermal necrolysis; vasculitis; angioedema; edema of the lips, face, neck, conjunctivae, hands or lower extremities; purpura; fever; chills; flushing; pruritus; urticaria; cutaneous candidiasis; vesicles; increased perspiration; hyperpigmentation; erythema nodosum; photosensitivity.

Allergic reactions ranging from urticaria to anaphylactic reactions have been reported. (See WARNINGS.)

SPECIAL SENSES: decreased visual acuity, blurred vision, disturbed vision (flashing lights, change in color perception, overbrightness of lights, diplopia), eye pain, anosmia, hearing loss, tinnitus, nystagmus, a bad taste.

MUSCULOSKELETAL: joint pain; jaw, arm or back pain; joint stiffness; neck and chest pain; achiness; flareup of gout.

RENAL/UROGENITAL: renal failure, interstitial nephritis, hemorrhagic cystitis, renal calculi, frequent urination, acidosis, urethral bleeding, polyuria, urinary retention, gynecomastia, candiduria, vaginitis. Crystalluria, cylindruria, hematuria, and albuminuria have also been reported.

CARDIOVASCULAR: cardiovascular collapse, cardiopulmonary arrest, myocardial infarction, arrhythmia, tachycardia, palpitation, cerebral thrombosis, syncope, cardiac murmur, hypertension, hypotension, angina pectoris.

RESPIRATORY: respiratory arrest, pulmonary embolism, dyspnea, pulmonary edema, respiratory distress, pleural effusion, hemoptysis, epistaxis, hiccough.

IV INFUSION SITE: thrombophlebitis, burning, pain, pruritus, paresthesia, erythema, swelling.

Also reported were agranulocytosis, prolongation of prothrombin time and possible exacerbation of myasthenia gravis.

Many of these events were described as only mild or moderate in severity, abated soon after the drug was discontinued and required no treatment.

In several instances, nausea, vomiting, tremor, irritability or palpitation were judged by investigators to be related to elevated serum levels of theophylline possibly as a result of drug interaction with ciprofloxacin.

**Adverse Laboratory Changes:** The most frequently reported changes in laboratory parameters with intravenous ciprofloxacin therapy, without regard to drug relationship, were:

| | | |
|---|---|---|
| Hepatic | — | Elevations of AST (SGOT), ALT (SGPT), alkaline phosphatase, LDH and serum bilirubin. |
| Hematologic | — | Elevated eosinophil and platelet counts, decreased platelet counts, hemoglobin and/or hematocrit. |
| Renal | — | Elevations of serum creatinine, BUN, uric acid. |
| Other | — | Elevations of serum creatine phosphokinase, serum theophylline (in patients receiving theophylline concomitantly), blood glucose, and triglycerides. |

Other changes occurring infrequently were: decreased leukocyte count, elevated atypical lymphocyte count, immature WBCs, elevated serum calcium, elevation of serum gamma-glutamyl transpeptidase (γ GT), decreased BUN, decreased uric acid, decreased total serum protein, decreased serum albumin, decreased serum potassium, elevated serum potassium, elevated serum cholesterol.

Other changes occurring rarely during administration of ciprofloxacin were: elevation of serum amylase, decrease of blood glucose, pancytopenia, leukocytosis, elevated sedimentation rate, change in serum phenytoin, decreased prothrombin time, hemolytic anemia, and bleeding diathesis.

## OVERDOSAGE

In the event of acute overdosage, the patient should be carefully observed and given supportive treatment. Adequate hydration must be maintained. Only a small amount of ciprofloxacin (<10%) is removed from the body after hemodialysis or peritoneal dialysis.

## DOSAGE AND ADMINISTRATION

The recommended adult dosage for urinary tract infections of mild to moderate severity is 200 mg every 12 hours. For severe or complicated urinary tract infections the recommended dosage is 400 mg every 12 hours.

The recommended adult dosage for lower respiratory tract infections, skin and skin structure infections and bone and joint infections of mild to moderate severity is 400 mg every 12 hours.

The determination of dosage for any particular patient must take into consideration the severity and nature of the infection, the susceptibility of the causative organism, the integrity of the patient's host-defense mechanisms and the status of renal and hepatic function.

### DOSAGE GUIDELINES

| Location of Infection | Type or Severity | Intravenous Unit Dose | Frequency | Daily Dose |
|---|---|---|---|---|
| Urinary tract | Mild/Moderate | 200 mg | q 12 h | 400 mg |
| | Severe/Complicated | 400 mg | q 12 h | 800 mg |
| Lower Respiratory tract; Skin and Skin Structure; Bone and Joint | Mild/Moderate | 400 mg | q 12 h | 800 mg |

**Cipro® I.V. should be administered by intravenous infusion over a period of 60 minutes.**

The duration of treatment depends upon the severity of infection. Generally, ciprofloxacin should be continued for at least 2 days after the signs and symptoms of infection have disappeared. The usual duration is 7 to 14 days. Bone and joint infections may require treatment for 4 to 6 weeks or longer.

Ciprofloxacin hydrochloride tablets (Cipro®) for oral administration are available. Parenteral therapy may be changed to oral Cipro® tablets when the condition warrants, at the discretion of the physician. For complete dosage and administration information, see Cipro® tablet package insert.

**Impaired Renal Function:** The following table provides dosage guidelines for use in patients with renal impairment; however, monitoring of serum drug levels provides the most reliable basis for dosage adjustment.

### RECOMMENDED STARTING AND MAINTENANCE DOSES FOR PATIENTS WITH IMPAIRED RENAL FUNCTION

| Creatinine Clearance (mL/min) | Dosage |
|---|---|
| ≥ 30 | See usual dosage |
| 5 – 29 | 200 – 400 mg q 18 – 24 hr |

When only the serum creatinine concentration is known, the following formula may be used to estimate creatinine clearance.

Men: Creatinine clearance (mL/min) = $\dfrac{\text{Weight (kg)} \times (140 - \text{age})}{72 \times \text{serum creatinine (mg/dL)}}$

Women: 0.85 × the value calculated for men.

The serum creatinine should represent a steady state of renal function.

For patients with changing renal function or for patients with renal impairment and hepatic insufficiency, measurement of serum concentrations of ciprofloxacin will provide additional guidance for adjusting dosage.

### INTRAVENOUS ADMINISTRATION

Cipro® I.V. should be administered by intravenous infusion over a period of 60 minutes. Slow infusion of a dilute solution into a large vein will minimize patient discomfort and reduce the risk of venous irritation.

**Vials (Injection Concentrate): THIS PREPARATION MUST BE DILUTED BEFORE USE.** The intravenous dose should be prepared by aseptically withdrawing the appropriate volume of concentrate from the vials of Cipro® I.V. This should be diluted with a suitable intravenous solution to a final concentration of 1–2 mg/mL. (See COMPATIBILITY AND STABILITY.) The resulting solution should be infused over a period of 60 minutes by direct infusion or through a Y-type intravenous infusion set which may already be in place.

If this method or the "piggyback" method of administration is used, it is advisable to discontinue temporarily the administration of any other solutions during the infusion of Cipro® I.V.

**Flexible Containers:** Cipro® I.V. is also available as a 0.2% premixed solution in 5% dextrose in flexible containers of 100 mL or 200 mL. The solutions in flexible containers may be infused as described above.

### COMPATIBILITY AND STABILITY

Ciprofloxacin injection 1% (10 mg/mL), when diluted with the following intravenous solutions to concentrations of 0.5 to 2.0 mg/mL, is stable for up to 14 days at refrigerated or room temperature storage.

0.9% Sodium Chloride Injection, USP
5% Dextrose Injection, USP

If Cipro® I.V. is to be given concomitantly with another drug, each drug should be given separately in accordance with the recommended dosage and route of administration for each drug.

### HOW SUPPLIED

Cipro® I.V. (ciprofloxacin) is available as a clear, colorless to slightly yellowish solution. Cipro® I.V. is available in 200 mg and 400 mg strengths. The concentrate is supplied in vials while the premixed solution is supplied in flexible containers as follows:

| CONTAINER | SIZE | STRENGTH | NDC NUMBER |
|---|---|---|---|
| Vial: | 20mL | 200 mg, 1% | 0026-8562-20 |
| | 40mL | 400 mg, 1% | 0026-8564-64 |
| Flexible Container: | 100mL 5% dextrose | 200 mg, 0.2% | 0026-8552-36 |
| | 200mL 5% dextrose | 400 mg, 0.2% | 0026-8554-63 |

### STORAGE

| | |
|---|---|
| Vials: | Store between 41 – 77°F (5 – 25°C). |
| Flexible Container: | Store between 41 – 77°F (5 – 25°C). |

Protect from light, avoid excessive heat, protect from freezing.

Ciprofloxacin is also available as Cipro® (ciprofloxacin HCl) Tablets 250, 500 and 750 mg.

### ANIMAL PHARMACOLOGY

Ciprofloxacin and other quinolones have been shown to cause arthropathy in immature animals of most species tested. (See WARNINGS.) Damage of weight-bearing joints was observed in juvenile dogs and rats. In young beagles, 100 mg/kg ciprofloxacin given daily for 4 weeks caused degenerative articular changes of the knee joint. At 30 mg/kg, the effect on the joint was minimal. In a subsequent study in beagles, removal of weight-bearing from the joint reduced the lesions but did not totally prevent them.

Crystalluria, sometimes associated with secondary nephropathy, occurs in laboratory animals dosed with ciprofloxacin. This is primarily related to the reduced solubility of ciprofloxacin under alkaline conditions, which predominate in the urine of test animals; in man, crystalluria is rare since human urine is typically acidic. In rhesus monkeys, crystalluria without nephropathy has been noted after intravenous doses as low as 5 mg/kg. After 6 months of intravenous dosing at 10 mg/kg/day, no nephropathological changes were noted; however, nephropathy was observed after dosing at 20 mg/kg/day for the same duration.

In dogs, ciprofloxacin administered at 3 and 10 mg/kg by rapid intravenous injection (15 sec.) produces pronounced hypotensive effects. These effects are considered to be related to histamine release because they are partially antagonized by pyrilamine, an antihistamine. In rhesus monkeys, rapid intravenous injection also produces hypotension, but the effect in this species is inconsistent and less pronounced.

In mice, concomitant administration of nonsteroidal anti-inflammatory drugs, such as fenbufen, phenylbutazone and indomethacin, with quinolones has been reported to enhance the CNS stimulatory effect of quinolones.

Ocular toxicity, seen with some related drugs, has not been observed in ciprofloxacin-treated animals.

Miles Inc.
Pharmaceutical Division
400 Morgan Lane
West Haven, CT 06516 USA

**Caution: Federal (USA) Law prohibits dispensing without a prescription.**

PZ100736   9/91   BAY q 3939   5202-4-A-U.S.-1   1628
© 1991 Miles Inc.   06-4745   Printed In U.S.A.

**References: 1.** Phillips I, King A. Comparative activity of the 4-quinolones. *Rev Infect Dis.* 1988;10(suppl 1):S70-S76. **2.** Auckenthaler R, Michéa-Hamzehpour M, Pechère JC. *In-vitro* activity of newer quinolones against aerobic bacteria. *J Antimicrob Chemother.* 1986;17(suppl B):29-39. **3.** Pernet A. Temafloxacin overview. In: *Temafloxacin: A New Standard in Quinolones.* New York, NY: AVMD Group; 1990:1-13.

# CIPRO®
## (ciprofloxacin hydrochloride)
## TABLETS

PZ100747

### DESCRIPTION

Cipro® (ciprofloxacin hydrochloride) is a synthetic broad spectrum antibacterial agent for oral administration. Ciprofloxacin, a fluoroquinolone, is available as the monohydrochloride monohydrate salt of 1-cyclopropyl-6-fluoro-1, 4-dihydro-4-oxo-7-(1-piperazinyl)-3-quinolinecarboxylic acid. It is a faintly yellowish to light yellow crystalline substance with a molecular weight of 385.8. Its empirical formula is $C_{17}H_{18}FN_3O_3 \cdot HCl \cdot H_2O$ and its chemical structure is as follows:

Cipro® is available in 250 mg, 500 mg and 750 mg (ciprofloxacin equivalent) film-coated tablets. The inactive ingredients are starch, microcrystalline cellulose, silicon dioxide, crospovidone, magnesium stearate, hydroxypropyl methylcellulose, titanium dioxide, polyethylene glycol and water. Ciprofloxacin differs from other quinolones in that it has a fluorine atom at the 6-position, a piperazine moiety at the 7-position, and a cyclopropyl ring at the 1-position.

### CLINICAL PHARMACOLOGY

Cipro® tablets are rapidly and well absorbed from the gastrointestinal tract after oral administration. The absolute bioavailability is approximately 70% with no substantial loss by first pass metabolism. Serum concentrations increase proportionally with the dose as shown:

| Dose (mg) | Maximum Serum Concentration (µg/mL) | Area Under Curve (AUC) (µg • hr/mL) |
|---|---|---|
| 250 | 1.2 | 4.8 |
| 500 | 2.4 | 11.6 |
| 750 | 4.3 | 20.2 |
| 1000 | 5.4 | 30.8 |

Maximum serum concentrations are attained 1 to 2 hours after oral dosing. Mean concentrations 12 hours after dosing with 250, 500, or 750 mg are 0.1, 0.2, and 0.4 µg/mL, respectively. The serum elimination half-life in subjects with normal renal function is approximately 4 hours.

Approximately 40 to 50% of an orally administered dose is excreted in the urine as unchanged drug. After a 250 mg oral dose, urine concentrations of ciprofloxacin usually exceed 200 µg/mL during the first two hours and are approximately 30 µg/mL at 8 to 12 hours after dosing. The urinary excretion of ciprofloxacin is virtually complete within 24 hours after dosing. The renal clearance of ciprofloxacin, which is approximately 300 mL/minute, exceeds the normal glomerular filtration rate of 120 mL/minute. Thus, active tubular secretion would seem to play a significant role in its elimination. Co-administration of probenecid with ciprofloxacin results in about a 50% reduction in the ciprofloxacin renal clearance and a 50% increase in its concentration in the systemic circulation. Although bile concentrations of ciprofloxacin are several fold higher than serum concentrations after oral dosing, only a small amount of the dose administered is recovered from the bile as unchanged drug. An additional 1-2% of the dose is recovered from the bile in the form of metabolites. Approximately 20 to 35% of an oral dose is recovered from the feces within 5 days after dosing. This may arise from either biliary clearance or transintestinal elimination. Four metabolites have been identified in human urine which together account for approximately 15% of an oral dose. The metabolites have antimicrobial activity, but are less active than unchanged ciprofloxacin.

When Cipro® is given concomitantly with food, there is a delay in the absorption of the drug, resulting in peak concentrations that are closer to 2 hours after dosing rather than 1 hour. The overall absorption, however, is not substantially affected. Concurrent administration of antacids containing magnesium hydroxide or aluminum hydroxide may reduce the bioavailability of ciprofloxacin by as much as 90%. (See PRECAUTIONS.)

Concomitant administration of ciprofloxacin with theophylline decreases the clearance of theophylline resulting in elevated serum theophylline levels, and increased risk of a patient developing CNS or other adverse reactions. Ciprofloxacin also decreases caffeine clearance and inhibits the formation of paraxanthine after caffeine administration. (See PRECAUTIONS.)

In patients with reduced renal function, the half-life of ciprofloxacin is slightly prolonged. Dosage adjustments may be required. (See DOSAGE AND ADMINISTRATION.)

In preliminary studies in patients with stable chronic liver cirrhosis, no significant changes in ciprofloxacin pharmacokinetics have been observed. The kinetics of ciprofloxacin in patients with acute hepatic insufficiency, however, have not been fully elucidated.

The binding of ciprofloxacin to serum proteins is 20 to 40% which is not likely to be high enough to cause significant protein binding interactions with other drugs.

After oral administration ciprofloxacin is widely distributed throughout the body. Tissue concentrations often exceed serum concentrations in both men and women, particularly in genital tissue including the prostate. Ciprofloxacin is present in active form in the saliva, nasal and bronchial secretions, sputum, skin blister fluid, lymph, peritoneal fluid, bile and prostatic secretions. Ciprofloxacin has also been detected in lung, skin, fat, muscle, cartilage, and bone. The drug diffuses into the cerebrospinal fluid (CSF); however, CSF concentrations are generally less than 10% of peak serum concentrations. Low levels of the drug have been detected in the aqueous and vitreous humors of the eye.

**Microbiology:** Ciprofloxacin has *in vitro* activity against a wide range of gram-negative and gram-positive organisms. The bactericidal action of ciprofloxacin results from interference with the enzyme DNA gyrase which is needed for the synthesis of bacterial DNA.

Ciprofloxacin has been shown to be active against most strains of the following organisms both *in vitro* and in clinical infections (See INDICATIONS AND USAGE section):

**Gram-positive bacteria**

Enterococcus faecalis (Many strains are only moderately susceptible)
Staphylococcus aureus
Staphylococcus epidermidis
Streptococcus pneumoniae
Streptococcus pyogenes

**Gram-negative bacteria**

Campylobacter jejuni
Citrobacter diversus
Citrobacter freundii
Enterobacter cloacae
Escherichia coli
Haemophilus influenzae
Haemophilus parainfluenzae
Klebsiella pneumoniae
Morganella morganii
Proteus mirabilis
Proteus vulgaris
Providencia rettgeri
Providencia stuartii
Pseudomonas aeruginosa
Serratia marcescens
Shigella flexneri
Shigella sonnei

Ciprofloxacin has been shown to be active *in vitro* against most strains of the following organisms; however, *the clinical significance of these data is unknown.*

**Gram-positive bacteria**

Staphylococcus haemolyticus
Staphylococcus hominis
Staphylococcus saprophyticus

**Gram-negative bacteria**

Acinetobacter calcoaceticus subs. anitrastus
Acinetobacter calcoaceticus subs. lwoffi
Aeromonas caviae
Aeromonas hydrophila
Brucella melitensis
Campylobacter coli
Edwardsiella tarda
Enterobacter aerogenes
Haemophilus ducreyi
Klebsiella oxytoca
Legionella pneumophila
Moraxella (Branhamella) catarrhalis
Neisseria gonorrhoeae
Neisseria meningitidis
Pasteurella multocida
Salmonella enteritidis
Salmonella typhi
Vibrio cholerae
Vibrio parahaemolyticus
Vibrio vulnificus
Yersinia enterocolitica

**Other organisms**

Chlamydia trachomatis (only moderately susceptible)
Mycobacterium tuberculosis (only moderately susceptible)

Most strains of *Pseudomonas cepacia* and some strains of *Xanthomonas (Pseudomonas) maltophilia* are resistant to ciprofloxacin as are most anaerobic bacteria, including *Bacteroides fragilis* and *Clostridium difficile.*

Ciprofloxacin is slightly less active when tested at acidic pH. The inoculum size has little effect when tested *in vitro*. The minimum bactericidal concentration (MBC) generally does not exceed the minimum inhibitory concentration (MIC) by more than a factor of 2. Resistance to ciprofloxacin *in vitro* develops slowly (multiple-step mutation).

Ciprofloxacin does not cross-react with other antimicrobial agents such as beta-lactams or aminoglycosides; therefore, organisms resistant to these drugs may be susceptible to ciprofloxacin.

*In vitro* studies have shown that additive activity often results when ciprofloxacin is combined with other antimicrobial agents such as beta-lactams, aminoglycosides, clindamycin, or metronidazole. Synergy has been reported particularly with the combination of ciprofloxacin and a beta-lactam; antagonism is observed only rarely.

**Susceptibility Tests**

**Diffusion Techniques:** Quantitative methods that require measurement of zone diameters give the most precise estimates of susceptibility of bacteria to antimicrobial agents. One such standardized procedure[1] which has been recommended for use with disks to test susceptibility of organisms to ciprofloxacin uses the 5-µg ciprofloxacin disk. Interpretation involves correlation of the diameters obtained in the disk test with the minimum inhibitory concentrations (MICs) for ciprofloxacin.

Reports from the laboratory giving results of the standard single-disk susceptibility test with a 5-µg ciprofloxacin disk should be interpreted according to the following criteria:

| Zone Diameter (mm) | Interpretation | |
|---|---|---|
| ≥ 21 | (S) | Susceptible |
| 16 – 20 | (I) | Intermediate (Moderately Susceptible) |
| ≤ 15 | (R) | Resistant |

A report of "Susceptible" indicates that the pathogen is likely to be inhibited by generally achievable blood levels. A report of "Intermediate (Moderately Susceptible)" suggests that the organism would be susceptible if high dosage is used or if the infection is confined to tissues and fluids in which high antimicrobial levels are attained. A report of "Resistant" indicates that achievable drug concentrations are unlikely to be inhibitory and other therapy should be selected.

**Dilution Techniques:** Use a standardized dilution method[2] (broth, agar, microdilution) or equivalent with ciprofloxacin powder. The MIC values obtained should be interpreted according to the following criteria:

| MIC (µg/mL) | Interpretation | |
|---|---|---|
| ≤ 1 | (S) | Susceptible |
| 2 | (I) | Intermediate (Moderately Susceptible) |
| ≥ 4 | (R) | Resistant |

Standardized procedures require the use of laboratory control organisms. This is true for both standardized diffusion techniques and standardized dilution techniques. The 5-µg ciprofloxacin disk should give the following zone diameters and the standard ciprofloxacin powder should provide the following MIC values:

| QC Strains | Disk Zone Diameter (mm) | MIC (µg/mL) |
|---|---|---|
| S. aureus (ATCC 25923) | 22 – 30 | — |
| S. aureus (ATCC 29213) | — | 0.12 – 0.5 |
| E. coli (ATCC 25922) | 30 – 40 | 0.004 – 0.015 |
| P. aeruginosa (ATCC 27853) | 25 – 33 | 0.25 – 1.0 |
| E. faecalis (ATCC 29212) | — | 0.25 – 2.0 |

For anaerobic bacteria the MIC of ciprofloxacin can be determined by agar or broth dilution (including microdilution) techniques[3].

### INDICATIONS AND USAGE

Cipro® is indicated for the treatment of infections caused by susceptible strains of the designated microorganisms in the conditions listed below. Please see DOSAGE AND ADMINISTRATION for specific recommendations.

**Lower Respiratory Infections** caused by *Escherichia coli, Klebsiella pneumoniae, Enterobacter cloacae, Proteus mirabilis, Pseudomonas aeruginosa, Haemophilus influenzae, Haemophilus parainfluenzae,* or *Streptococcus pneumoniae.*

**Skin and Skin Structure Infections** caused by *Escherichia coli, Klebsiella pneumoniae, Enterobacter cloacae, Proteus mirabilis, Proteus vulgaris, Providencia stuartii, Morganella morganii, Citrobacter freundii, Pseudomonas aeruginosa, Staphylococcus aureus, Staphylococcus epidermidis,* or *Streptococcus pyogenes.*

**Bone and Joint Infections** caused by *Enterobacter cloacae, Serratia marcescens,* or *Pseudomonas aeruginosa.*

**Urinary Tract Infections** caused by *Escherichia coli, Klebsiella pneumoniae, Enterobacter cloacae, Serratia marcescens, Proteus mirabilis, Providencia rettgeri, Morganella morganii, Citrobacter diversus, Citrobacter freundii, Pseudomonas aeruginosa, Staphylococcus epidermidis,* or *Enterococcus faecalis.*

**Infectious Diarrhea** caused by *Escherichia coli* (enterotoxigenic strains), *Campylobacter jejuni, Shigella flexneri\** or *Shigella sonnei\** when antibacterial therapy is indicated.

*\*Although treatment of infections due to this organism in this organ system demonstrated a clinically significant outcome, efficacy was studied in fewer than 10 patients.*

If anaerobic organisms are suspected of contributing to the infection, appropriate therapy should be administered.

Appropriate culture and susceptibility tests should be performed before treatment in order to isolate and identify organisms causing infection and to determine their susceptibility to ciprofloxacin. Therapy with Cipro® may be initiated before results of these tests are known; once results become available appropriate therapy should be continued. As with other drugs, some strains of *Pseudomonas aeruginosa* may develop resistance fairly rapidly during treatment with ciprofloxacin. Culture and susceptibility testing performed periodically during therapy will provide information not only on the therapeutic effect of the antimicrobial agent but also on the possible emergence of bacterial resistance.

## CONTRAINDICATIONS

Cipro® (ciprofloxacin hydrochloride) is contraindicated in persons with a history of hypersensitivity to ciprofloxacin or any member of the quinolone class of antimicrobial agents.

## WARNINGS

**THE SAFETY AND EFFECTIVENESS OF CIPROFLOXACIN IN CHILDREN, ADOLESCENTS (LESS THAN 18 YEARS OF AGE), PREGNANT WOMEN, AND LACTATING WOMEN HAVE NOT BEEN ESTABLISHED. (SEE PRECAUTIONS-PEDIATRIC USE, PREGNANCY AND NURSING MOTHERS SUBSECTIONS.)** The oral administration of ciprofloxacin caused lameness in immature dogs. Histopathological examination of the weight-bearing joints of these dogs revealed permanent lesions of the cartilage. Related quinolone-class drugs also produce erosions of cartilage of weight-bearing joints and other signs of arthropathy in immature animals of various species. (See ANIMAL PHARMACOLOGY.)

Convulsions have been reported in patients receiving ciprofloxacin. Convulsions, increased intracranial pressure, and toxic psychosis have been reported in patients receiving drugs in this class. Quinolones may also cause central nervous system (CNS) stimulation which may lead to tremors, restlessness, lightheadedness, confusion and hallucinations. If these reactions occur in patients receiving ciprofloxacin, the drug should be discontinued and appropriate measures instituted. As with all quinolones, ciprofloxacin should be used with caution in patients with known or suspected CNS disorders, such as severe cerebral arteriosclerosis, epilepsy, and other factors that predispose to seizures. (See ADVERSE REACTIONS.)

**SERIOUS AND FATAL REACTIONS HAVE BEEN REPORTED IN PATIENTS RECEIVING CONCURRENT ADMINISTRATION OF CIPROFLOXACIN AND THEOPHYLLINE.** These reactions have included cardiac arrest, seizure, status epilepticus and respiratory failure. Although similar serious adverse events have been reported in patients receiving theophylline alone, the possibility that these reactions may be potentiated by ciprofloxacin cannot be eliminated. If concomitant use cannot be avoided, serum levels of theophylline should be monitored and dosage adjustments made as appropriate.

Serious and occasionally fatal hypersensitivity (anaphylactic) reactions, some following the first dose, have been reported in patients receiving quinolone therapy. Some reactions were accompanied by cardiovascular collapse, loss of consciousness, tingling, pharyngeal or facial edema, dyspnea, urticaria, and itching. Only a few patients had a history of hypersensitivity reactions. Serious anaphylactic reactions require immediate emergency treatment with epinephrine. Oxygen, intravenous steroids, and airway management, including intubation, should be administered as indicated.

Severe hypersensitivity reactions characterized by rash, fever, eosinophilia, jaundice, and hepatic necrosis with fatal outcome have also been rarely reported in patients receiving ciprofloxacin along with other drugs. The possibility that these reactions were related to ciprofloxacin cannot be excluded. Ciprofloxacin should be discontinued at the first appearance of a skin rash or any other sign of hypersensitivity.

**Pseudomembranous colitis has been reported with nearly all antibacterial agents, including ciprofloxacin, and may range in severity from mild to life-threatening. Therefore, it is important to consider this diagnosis in patients who present with diarrhea subsequent to the administration of antibacterial agents.**

Treatment with antibacterial agents alters the normal flora of the colon and may permit overgrowth of clostridia. Studies indicate that a toxin produced by *Clostridium difficile* is one primary cause of "antibiotic-associated colitis".

After the diagnosis of pseudomembranous colitis has been established, therapeutic measures should be initiated. Mild cases of pseudomembranous colitis usually respond to drug discontinuation alone. In moderate to severe cases, consideration should be given to management with fluids and electrolytes, protein supplementation and treatment with an antibacterial drug clinically effective against *C. difficile* colitis.

## PRECAUTIONS

**General:** Crystals of ciprofloxacin have been observed rarely in the urine of human subjects but more frequently in the urine of laboratory animals, which is usually alkaline. (See ANIMAL PHARMACOLOGY.) Crystalluria related to ciprofloxacin has been reported only rarely in humans because human urine is usually acidic. Alkalinity of the urine should be avoided in patients receiving ciprofloxacin. Patients should be well hydrated to prevent the formation of highly concentrated urine.

Alteration of the dosage regimen is necessary for patients with impairment of renal function. (See DOSAGE AND ADMINISTRATION.)

Moderate to severe phototoxicity manifested by an exaggerated sunburn reaction has been observed in patients who are exposed to direct sunlight while receiving some members of the quinolone class of drugs. Excessive sunlight should be avoided. Therapy should be discontinued if phototoxicity occurs.

As with any potent drug, periodic assessment of organ system functions, including renal, hepatic, and hematopoietic function, is advisable during prolonged therapy.

**Information for Patients:** Patients should be advised that ciprofloxacin may be taken with or without meals. The preferred time of dosing is two hours after a meal. Patients should also be advised to drink fluids liberally and not take antacids containing magnesium, aluminum, or calcium, products containing iron, or multivitamins containing zinc. However, usual dietary intake of calcium has not been shown to alter the absorption of ciprofloxacin.

Patients should be advised that ciprofloxacin may be associated with hypersensitivity reactions, even following a single dose, and to discontinue the drug at the first sign of a skin rash or other allergic reaction.

Patients should be advised to avoid excessive sunlight or artificial ultraviolet light while receiving ciprofloxacin and to discontinue therapy if phototoxicity occurs.

Ciprofloxacin may cause dizziness and lightheadedness; therefore patients should know how they react to this drug before they operate an automobile or machinery or engage in activities requiring mental alertness or coordination.

Patients should be advised that ciprofloxacin may increase the effects of theophylline and caffeine. There is a possibility of caffeine accumulation when products containing caffeine are consumed while taking quinolones.

**Drug Interactions:** As with some other quinolones, concurrent administration of ciprofloxacin with theophylline may lead to elevated serum concentrations of theophylline and prolongation of its elimination half-life. This may result in increased risk of theophylline-related adverse reactions. (See WARNINGS.) If concomitant use cannot be avoided, serum levels of theophylline should be monitored and dosage adjustments made as appropriate.

Some quinolones, including ciprofloxacin, have also been shown to interfere with the metabolism of caffeine. This may lead to reduced clearance of caffeine and a prolongation of its serum half-life.

Concurrent administration of ciprofloxacin with antacids containing magnesium, aluminum, or calcium; with sucralfate or divalent and trivalent cations such as iron may substantially interfere with the absorption of ciprofloxacin, resulting in serum and urine levels considerably lower than desired. To a lesser extent this effect is demonstrated with zinc-containing multivitamins. (See DOSAGE AND ADMINISTRATION for concurrent administration of these agents with ciprofloxacin.)

Some quinolones, including ciprofloxacin, have been associated with transient elevations in serum creatinine in patients receiving cyclosporine concomitantly.

Quinolones have been reported to enhance the effects of the oral anticoagulant warfarin or its derivatives. When these products are administered concomitantly, prothrombin time or other suitable coagulation tests should be closely monitored.

Probenecid interferes with renal tubular secretion of ciprofloxacin and produces an increase in the level of ciprofloxacin in the serum. This should be considered if patients are receiving both drugs concomitantly.

As with other broad spectrum antimicrobial agents, prolonged use of ciprofloxacin may result in overgrowth of nonsusceptible organisms. Repeated evaluation of the patient's condition and microbial susceptibility testing is essential. If superinfection occurs during therapy, appropriate measures should be taken.

**Carcinogenesis, Mutagenesis, Impairment of Fertility:** Eight *in vitro* mutagenicity tests have been conducted with ciprofloxacin and the test results are listed below:

Salmonella/Microsome Test (Negative)
*E. coli* DNA Repair Assay (Negative)
Mouse Lymphoma Cell Forward Mutation Assay (Positive)
Chinese Hamster $V_{79}$ Cell HGPRT Test (Negative)
Syrian Hamster Embryo Cell Transformation Assay (Negative)
*Saccharomyces cerevisiae* Point Mutation Assay (Negative)
*Saccharomyces cerevisiae* Mitotic Crossover and Gene Conversion Assay (Negative)
Rat Hepatocyte DNA Repair Assay (Positive)

Thus 2 of the 8 tests were positive but results of the following 3 *in vivo* test systems gave negative results:

Rat Hepatocyte DNA Repair Assay
Micronucleus Test (Mice)
Dominant Lethal Test (Mice)

Long term carcinogenicity studies in mice and rats have been completed. After daily oral dosing for up to 2 years, there is no evidence that ciprofloxacin had any carcinogenic or tumorigenic effects in these species.

**Pregnancy: Teratogenic Effects. Pregnancy Category C:** Reproduction studies have been performed in rats and mice at doses up to 6 times the usual daily human dose and have revealed no evidence of impaired fertility or harm to the fetus due to ciprofloxacin. In rabbits, as with most antimicrobial agents, ciprofloxacin (30 and 100 mg/kg orally) produced gastrointestinal disturbances resulting in maternal weight loss and an increased incidence of abortion. No teratogenicity was observed at either dose. After intravenous administration, at doses up to 20 mg/kg, no maternal toxicity was produced, and no embryotoxicity or teratogenicity was observed. There are, however, no adequate and well-controlled studies in pregnant women. Ciprofloxacin should be used during pregnancy only if the potential benefit justifies the potential risk to the fetus. (See WARNINGS.)

**Nursing Mothers:** Ciprofloxacin is excreted in human milk. Because of the potential for serious adverse reactions in infants nursing from mothers taking ciprofloxacin, a decision should be made either to discontinue nursing or to discontinue the drug, taking into account the importance of the drug to the mother.

**Pediatric Use:** Safety and effectiveness in children and adolescents less than 18 years of age have not been established. Ciprofloxacin causes arthropathy in juvenile animals. (See WARNINGS.)

## ADVERSE REACTIONS

During clinical investigation, 2,799 patients received 2,868 courses of the drug. Adverse events that were considered likely to be drug related occurred in 7.3% of patients treated, possibly related in 9.2% (total of 16.5% thought to be possibly or probably related to drug therapy), and remotely related in 3.0%. Ciprofloxacin was discontinued because of an adverse event in 3.5% of patients treated, primarily involving the gastrointestinal system (1.5%), skin (0.6%), and central nervous system (0.4%).

The most frequently reported events, drug related or not, were nausea (5.2%), diarrhea (2.3%), vomiting (2.0%), abdominal pain/discomfort (1.7%), headache (1.2%), restlessness (1.1%), and rash (1.1%).

Additional events that occurred in less than 1% of ciprofloxacin treated patients are listed below.

CARDIOVASCULAR: palpitation, atrial flutter, ventricular ectopy, syncope, hypertension, angina pectoris, myocardial infarction, cardiopulmonary arrest, cerebral thrombosis
CENTRAL NERVOUS SYSTEM: dizziness, lightheadedness, insomnia, nightmares, hallucinations, manic reaction, irritability, tremor, ataxia, convulsive seizures, lethargy, drowsiness, weakness, malaise, anorexia, phobia, depersonalization, depression, paresthesia (See above.) (See PRECAUTIONS.)

GASTROINTESTINAL: painful oral mucosa, oral candidiasis, dysphagia, intestinal perforation, gastrointestinal bleeding (See above.) Cholestatic jaundice has been reported.

MUSCULOSKELETAL: joint or back pain, joint stiffness, achiness, neck or chest pain, flare up of gout

RENAL/UROGENITAL: interstitial nephritis, nephritis, renal failure, polyuria, urinary retention, urethral bleeding, vaginitis, acidosis

RESPIRATORY: dyspnea, epistaxis, laryngeal or pulmonary edema, hiccough, hemoptysis, bronchospasm, pulmonary embolism

SKIN/HYPERSENSITIVITY: pruritus, urticaria, photosensitivity, flushing, fever, chills, angioedema, edema of the face, neck, lips, conjunctivae or hands, cutaneous candidiasis, hyperpigmentation, erythema nodosum (See above.)

Allergic reactions ranging from urticaria to anaphylactic reactions have been reported. (See WARNINGS.)

SPECIAL SENSES: blurred vision, disturbed vision (change in color perception, overbrightness of lights), decreased visual acuity, diplopia, eye pain, tinnitus, hearing loss, bad taste

Most of the adverse events reported were described as only mild or moderate in severity, abated soon after the drug was discontinued, and required no treatment.

In several instances nausea, vomiting, tremor, irritability or palpitation were judged by investigators to be related to elevated serum levels of theophylline possibly as a result of drug interaction with ciprofloxacin.

Other adverse events reported in the postmarketing phase include anaphylactic reactions, erythema multiforme/Stevens-Johnson syndrome, exfoliative dermatitis, toxic epidermal necrolysis, vasculitis, jaundice, hepatic necrosis, toxic psychosis, postural hypotension, possible exacerbation of myasthenia gravis, anosmia, confusion, dysphasia, nystagmus, pseudomembranous colitis, pancreatitis, dyspepsia, flatulence, and constipation. Also reported were hemolytic anemia; agranulocytosis; elevation of serum triglycerides, serum cholesterol, blood glucose, serum potassium; prolongation of prothrombin time; albuminuria; candiduria, vaginal candidiasis; renal calculi; and change in serum phenytoin. (See PRECAUTIONS.)

**Adverse Laboratory Changes:** Changes in laboratory parameters listed as adverse events without regard to drug relationship:

Hepatic — Elevations of: ALT (SGPT) (1.9%), AST (SGOT) (1.7%), alkaline phosphatase (0.8%), LDH (0.4%), serum bilirubin (0.3%).

Hematologic — Eosinophilia (0.6%), leukopenia (0.4%), decreased blood platelets (0.1%), elevated blood platelets (0.1%), pancytopenia (0.1%).

Renal — Elevations of: Serum creatinine (1.1%), BUN (0.9%). CRYSTALLURIA, CYLINDRURIA AND HEMATURIA HAVE BEEN REPORTED.

Other changes occurring in less than 0.1% of patients treated were: Elevation of serum gammaglutamyl transferase, elevation of serum amylase, reduction in blood glucose, elevated uric acid, decrease in hemoglobin, anemia, bleeding diathesis, increase in blood monocytes, leukocytosis.

### OVERDOSAGE

In the event of acute overdosage, the stomach should be emptied by inducing vomiting or by gastric lavage. The patient should be carefully observed and given supportive treatment. Adequate hydration must be maintained. Only a small amount of ciprofloxacin (<10%) is removed from the body after hemodialysis or peritoneal dialysis.

### DOSAGE AND ADMINISTRATION

The usual adult dosage for patients with urinary tract infections is 250 mg every 12 hours. For patients with complicated infections caused by organisms not highly susceptible, 500 mg may be administered every 12 hours.

Lower respiratory tract infections, skin and skin structure infections, and bone and joint infections may be treated with 500 mg every 12 hours. For more severe or complicated infections, a dosage of 750 mg may be given every 12 hours.

The recommended dosage for Infectious Diarrhea is 500 mg every 12 hours.

### DOSAGE GUIDELINES

| Location of Infection | Type or Severity | Unit Dose | Frequency | Daily Dose |
|---|---|---|---|---|
| Urinary tract | Mild/Moderate | 250 mg | q 12 h | 500 mg |
| | Severe/Complicated | 500 mg | q 12 h | 1000 mg |
| Lower respiratory tract; | Mild/Moderate | 500 mg | q 12 h | 1000 mg |
| Bone and Joint; | Severe/Complicated | 750 mg | q 12 h | 1500 mg |
| Skin or Skin Structure | | | | |
| Infectious Diarrhea | Mild/Moderate/Severe | 500 mg | q 12 h | 1000 mg |

The determination of dosage for any particular patient must take into consideration the severity and nature of the infection, the susceptibility of the causative organism, the integrity of the patient's host-defense mechanisms, and the status of renal function and hepatic function.

The duration of treatment depends upon the severity of infection. Generally ciprofloxacin should be continued for at least 2 days after the signs and symptoms of infection have disappeared. The usual duration is 7 to 14 days; however, for severe and complicated infections more prolonged therapy may be required. Bone and joint infections may require treatment for 4 to 6 weeks or longer. Infectious Diarrhea may be treated for 5-7 days.

**Concurrent Use With Antacids or Multivalent Cations:** Concurrent administration of ciprofloxacin with sucralfate or divalent and trivalent cations such as iron or antacids containing magnesium, aluminum, or calcium may substantially interfere with the absorption of ciprofloxacin, resulting in serum and urine levels considerably lower than desired. Therefore, concurrent administration of these agents with ciprofloxacin should be avoided. However, usual dietary intake of calcium has not been shown to alter the bioavailability of ciprofloxacin. Single dose bioavailability studies have shown that antacids may be administered either 2 hours after or 6 hours before ciprofloxacin dosing without a significant decrease in bioavailability. Histamine $H_2$-receptor antagonists appear to have no significant effect on the bioavailability of ciprofloxacin.

**Impaired Renal Function:** Ciprofloxacin is eliminated primarily by renal excretion; however, the drug is also metabolized and partially cleared through the biliary system of the liver and through the intestine. These alternate pathways of drug elimination appear to compensate for the reduced renal excretion in patients with renal impairment. Nonetheless, some modification of dosage is recommended, particularly for patients with severe renal dysfunction. The following table provides dosage guidelines for use in patients with renal impairment; however, monitoring of serum drug levels provides the most reliable basis for dosage adjustment:

### RECOMMENDED STARTING AND MAINTENANCE DOSES FOR PATIENTS WITH IMPAIRED RENAL FUNCTION

| Creatinine Clearance (mL/min) | Dose |
|---|---|
| > 50 | See Usual Dosage |
| 30 – 50 | 250 – 500 mg q 12 h |
| 5 – 29 | 250 – 500 mg q 18 h |
| Patients on hemodialysis or Peritoneal dialysis | 250 – 500 mg q 24 h (after dialysis) |

When only the serum creatinine concentration is known, the following formula may be used to estimate creatinine clearance.

$$\text{Men: Creatinine clearance (mL/min)} = \frac{\text{Weight (kg)} \times (140 - \text{age})}{72 \times \text{serum creatinine (mg/dL)}}$$

Women: 0.85 × the value calculated for men.

The serum creatinine should represent a steady state of renal function.

In patients with severe infections and severe renal impairment, a unit dose of 750 mg may be administered at the intervals noted above; however, patients should be carefully monitored and the serum ciprofloxacin concentration should be measured periodically. Peak concentrations (1-2 hours after dosing) should generally range from 2 to 4 µg/mL.

For patients with changing renal function or for patients with renal impairment and hepatic insufficiency, measurement of serum concentrations of ciprofloxacin will provide additional guidance for adjusting dosage.

### HOW SUPPLIED

Cipro® (ciprofloxacin hydrochloride) is available as round, slightly yellowish film-coated tablets containing 250 mg ciprofloxacin. The 250 mg tablet is coded with the word "Miles" on one side and "512" on the reverse side. Cipro® is also available as capsule shaped, slightly yellowish film-coated tablets containing 500 mg or 750 mg ciprofloxacin. The 500 mg tablet is coded with the word "Miles" on one side and "513" on the reverse side; the 750 mg tablet is coded with the word "Miles" on one side and "514" on the reverse side. Available in bottles of 50's, 100's and in Unit Dose packages of 100.

| | Strength | NDC Code | Tablet Identification |
|---|---|---|---|
| Bottles of 50: | 750 mg | NDC 0026-8514-50 | Miles 514 |
| Bottles of 100: | 250 mg | NDC 0026-8512-51 | Miles 512 |
| | 500 mg | NDC 0026-8513-51 | Miles 513 |
| Unit Dose Package of 100: | 250 mg | NDC 0026-8512-48 | Miles 512 |
| | 500 mg | NDC 0026-8513-48 | Miles 513 |
| | 750 mg | NDC 0026-8514-48 | Miles 514 |

**Store below 86°F (30°C).**

### ANIMAL PHARMACOLOGY

Ciprofloxacin and other quinolones have been shown to cause arthropathy in immature animals of most species tested. (See WARNINGS.) Damage of weight bearing joints was observed in juvenile dogs and rats. In young beagles 100 mg/kg ciprofloxacin, given daily for 4 weeks, caused degenerative articular changes of the knee joint. At 30 mg/kg the effect on the joint was minimal. In a subsequent study in beagles removal of weight bearing from the joint reduced the lesions but did not totally prevent them.

Crystalluria, sometimes associated with secondary nephropathy, occurs in laboratory animals dosed with ciprofloxacin. This is primarily related to the reduced solubility of ciprofloxacin under alkaline conditions, which predominate in the urine of test animals; in man, crystalluria is rare since human urine is typically acidic. In rhesus monkeys, crystalluria without nephropathy has been noted after single oral doses as low as 5 mg/kg. After 6 months of intravenous dosing at 10 mg/kg/day, no nephropathological changes were noted; however, nephropathy was observed after dosing at 20 mg/kg/day for the same duration.

In dogs, ciprofloxacin at 3 and 10 mg/kg by rapid IV injection (15 sec.) produces pronounced hypotensive effects. These effects are considered to be related to histamine release since they are partially antagonized by pyrilamine, an antihistamine. In rhesus monkeys, rapid IV injection also produces hypotension but the effect in this species is inconsistent and less pronounced.

In mice, concomitant administration of nonsteroidal anti-inflammatory drugs such as fenbufen, phenylbutazone and indomethacin with quinolones has been reported to enhance the CNS stimulatory effect of quinolones.

Ocular toxicity seen with some related drugs has not been observed in ciprofloxacin-treated animals.

**References: 1.** National Committee for Clinical Laboratory Standards, _Performance Standards for Antimicrobial Disk Susceptibility Tests_-Fourth Edition. Approved Standard NCCLS Document M2-A4, Vol. 10, No. 7, NCCLS, Villanova, PA, April, 1990. **2.** National Committee for Clinical Laboratory Standards, _Methods for Dilution Antimicrobial Susceptibility Tests for Bacteria that Grow Aerobically_-Second Edition. Approved Standard NCCLS Document M7-A2, Vol. 10, No. 8, NCCLS, Villanova, PA, April, 1990. **3.** National Committee for Clinical Laboratory Standards, _Methods for Antimicrobial Susceptibility Testing of Anaerobic Bacteria_-Second Edition. Approved Standard NCCLS Document M11-A2, Vol. 10, No. 15, NCCLS, Villanova, PA, December, 1990.

Miles Inc.
Pharmaceutical Division
400 Morgan Lane
West Haven, CT 06516 USA

**Caution: Federal (USA) Law prohibits dispensing without a prescription.**

PZ100747        1/93        Bay o 9867        5202-2-A-U.S.-4
© 1993 Miles Inc.                  2545                Printed in USA